Sailing Along

CHARLES C. WALCUTT
GLENN McCRACKEN

Consultants:
SISTER ELEANOR GRANGER
CYNTHIA JENKINS
ALLAN MORASCH

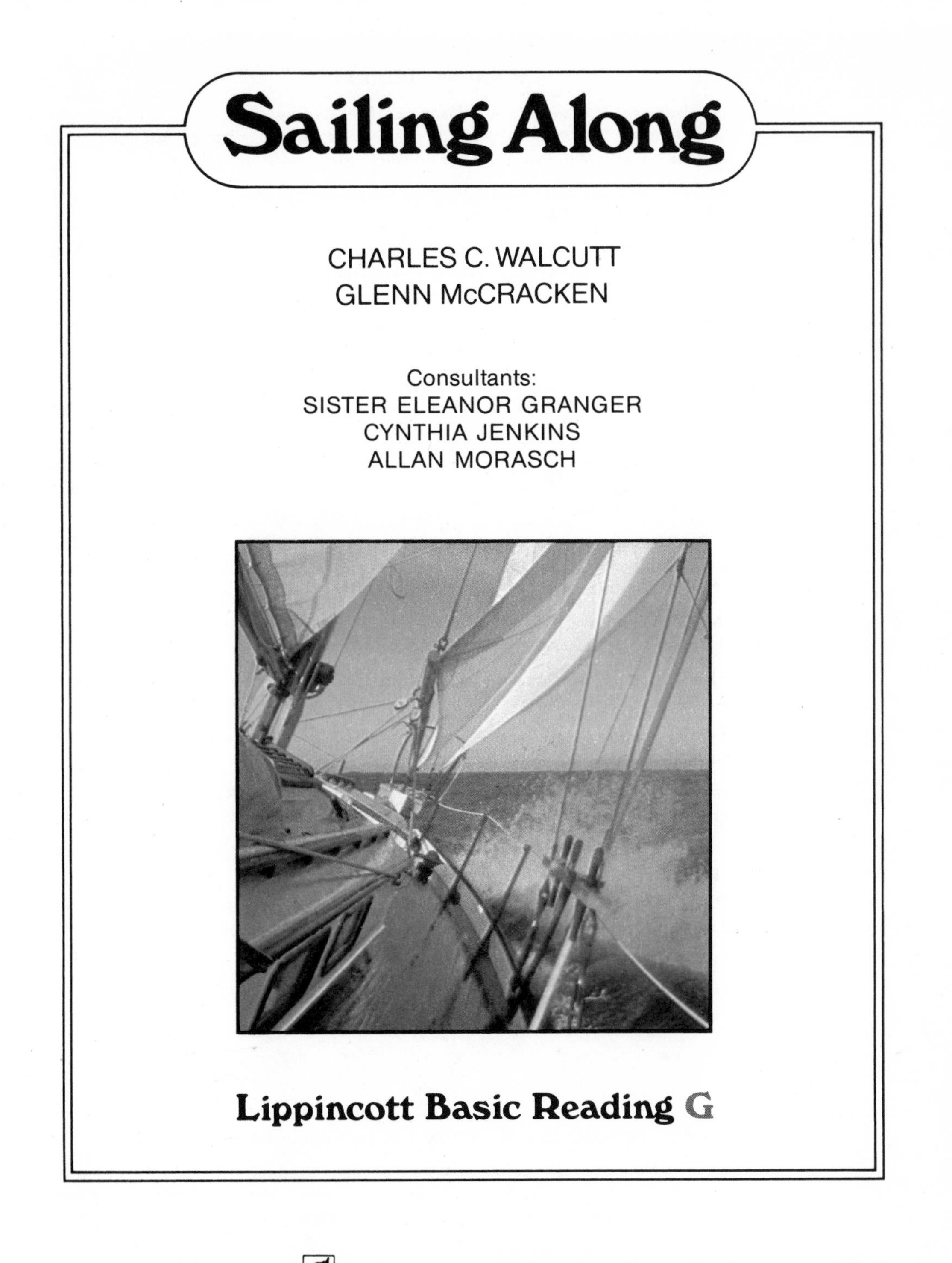

Lippincott Basic Reading G

HARPER & ROW, Publishers 1817 New York Philadelphia Hagerstown San Francisco London

ACKNOWLEDGMENTS

Grateful acknowledgment is made to the following authors and publishers for use of copyrighted materials. Every effort has been made to obtain permission to use previously published material. Any errors or omissions are unintentional and the Publisher will be grateful to learn of them.

"Dancer" adapted by permission of Charles Scribner's Sons from *Sometimes I Dance Mountains* by Byrd Baylor. Copyright © 1973 Byrd Baylor.

"Shades of the Past" excerpted from the book *The Heritage Sampler: A Book of Colonial Arts & Crafts* by Cheryl Hoople. Copyright © 1975 by Cheryl Hoople. Reprinted by permission of The Dial Press.

"Yagua Days" adapted from *Yagua Days* by Cruz Martel. Copyright © 1976 by Cruz Martel. Reprinted by permission of The Dial Press.

"The Acrobats" and "The Flying Festoon" from *Where the Sidewalk Ends: The Poems and Drawings of Shel Silverstein.* Copyright © 1974 by Shel Silverstein. By permission of Harper & Row, Publishers, Inc.

Text adaptation of "The Mystery Marble" from *Magic Secrets* by Rose Wyler and Gerald Ames. Text copyright © 1967 by Rose Wyler and Gerald Ames. An I Can Read Book. By permission of Harper & Row, Publishers, Inc.

"The Falling Star" reprinted with permission of Macmillan Publishing Co., Inc. from *Collected Poems* by Sara Teasdale. Copyright 1930 by Sara Teasdale Filsinger, renewed 1958 by Guaranty Trust Co. of New York, Executor.

"Angry" by Marci Ridlon from *That Was Summer.* Copyright © 1969 by the Follett Publishing Company. Reprinted by permission of Marci Ridlon.

"If I were a cricket, . . ." and "If I were a spider, . . ." from *If I Were a Cricket . . .* by Kazue Mizumura. Copyright © 1973 by Kazue Mizumura. By permission of Thomas Y. Crowell, Publishers.

Adapted text of *The Seeing Stick* by Jane Yolen. Copyright © 1977 by Jane Yolen. By permission of Thomas Y. Crowell, Publishers.

"Thalia Brown and the Blue Bug" adapted from *Thalia Brown and the Blue Bug,* text © 1979, by Michelle Dionetti, by permission of Addison-Wesley Publishing Company, Inc.

"Take It or Leave It" adapted with permission from the book *Take It or Leave It* by Osmond Molarsky, copyright 1971. Published by David McKay Co., Inc.

"The Magic Balloon" adapted from *Funny Magic, Easy Tricks for Young Magicians,* by Rose Wyler and Gerald Ames. Text copyright © 1972 by Rose Wyler and Gerald Ames. By permission of Four Winds Press, a division of Scholastic Inc.

(continued on page 283)

Printed in the United States of America

ISBN 0–397–44049–9

Contents

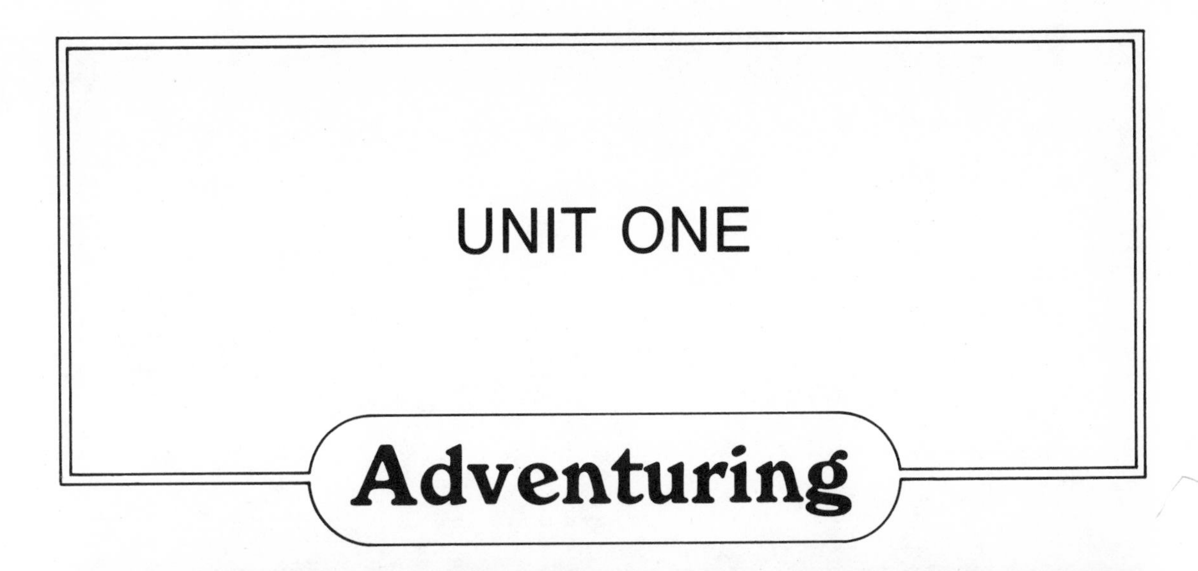

UNIT ONE

Adventuring

How Bambi Found the Meadow

by Felix Salten

Bambi walked behind his mother on a narrow track that ran through the midst of the bushes. How pleasant it was to walk there! The thick, leafy branches stroked his sides softly and lightly.

The track appeared to be blocked in a dozen places and yet they were able to walk with ease. There were tracks like this everywhere, running crisscross through the whole woods.

His mother knew them all. Sometimes Bambi stopped before a bush which blocked the path, but his mother always knew where the path went through without pausing or searching.

They walked on. Bambi was in good spirits and felt like leaping off the path, but he stayed close to his mother.

Bambi loved to question his mother and then hear what answer she would give. But today she was walking very quickly. Bambi had to hurry to keep up with her.

Loud cries were coming from a young ash tree which stood near their path. The mother went along without noticing them, but Bambi stopped curiously. Overhead, two jays were quarreling about a nest they had robbed.

"Get away, you robber!" cried one.

"Keep cool, you fool," the other answered. "I'm not afraid of you."

"Look for your own nests," the first one shouted. He was shaking with anger. "What bad manners!" he chattered. "What bad manners!"

The other jay saw Bambi and fluttered down a few branches to shout at him. "What are you staring at?" he screamed.

Bambi sprang away terrified. He reached his mother and walked behind her again, frightened and obedient, hoping she had not seen him stopping.

After a pause he asked, "Mother, what are bad manners?"

"I don't know," said his mother.

Bambi thought a while; then he began again. "Why were they both so angry with each other, Mother?" he asked.

"They were fighting over food," his mother answered.

"Will we fight over food, too, sometime?" Bambi asked.

"No," said his mother.

Bambi asked, "Why not?"

"Because there is enough for all of us," his mother replied.

Bambi wanted to know something else. "Mother," he began.

"What is it?"

"Will we be angry with each other sometime?" he asked.

"No, child," said his mother, "we don't do such things."

The Meadow

They walked along again. Soon it grew light ahead of them. The trail ended.

A few steps more and they would be in a bright open space. Bambi wanted to jump forward, but his mother stopped.

"What is it?" he asked.

"It's the meadow," his mother answered.

"What is a meadow?" asked Bambi again.

His mother cut him short. "You'll soon find out," she said. She had become very serious. She stood still, holding her head high and listening. She breathed deeply and looked worried.

"It's all right," she said at last. "We can go out."

Bambi leaped forward, but his mother blocked the way.

"Wait until I call you," she said. Bambi obeyed and stood still. "That's right," said his mother, "and now listen to me." Bambi heard how seriously his mother spoke and felt very excited.

"Walking on the meadow is not so simple," his mother went on. "It's a hard and dangerous activity. Don't ask me why. You'll find out later on. Now do exactly as I tell you to. Will you?"

"Yes," Bambi promised.

"Good," said his mother. "I'm going out alone first. Stay here and wait. And don't take your eyes off me for a minute. If you see me run back here, then turn around and run as fast as you can. I'll catch up with you soon." She grew silent and seemed to be thinking. Then she went on, "Run away as fast as your legs will carry you. Run even if something should happen . . . even if you see me fall to the ground . . . do not think of me, do you understand?

No matter what you see or hear, start running right away, just as fast as you can. Do you promise me you'll do that?"

She spoke so seriously that Bambi replied, "Yes."

She went on speaking. "Out there if I should call you," she said, "there must be no looking around and no questions, but you must get behind me at once. Understand that. Run without pausing or stopping to think. If I begin to run, that means for you to run, too, and no stopping, until we are back here again. You won't forget, will you?"

"No," said Bambi in a troubled voice.

"Now, I'm going ahead," said his mother, and she seemed to become calmer.

She walked out. Bambi, who never took his eyes off her, saw how she moved forward with slow, careful steps. He stood there, full of fear and curiosity. He saw how his mother listened in all directions. Then she grew calm again. She stretched herself forward. Then she looked around satisfied and called, "Come!"

Bambi jumped out. Joy seized him with such a great force that he forgot his worries. In the thicket he could see only the green treetops overhead. Only once in a while could he see the blue sky.

Now he saw the whole heaven over his head. He was glad without knowing why. In the forest, he had seen only a stray sunbeam now and then, or a ray of light coming through the branches. Suddenly he was standing in the blinding hot sunlight. He stood in the wonderful warmth that made him shut his eyes, but open his heart. He was so happy.

Bambi was simply wild. He leaped into the air three, four, five times. He had to do it. He felt a terrible desire to leap and jump. He stretched his young limbs joyfully. He drank in the air. The sweet smell of the meadow made him so happy that he jumped into the air.

His mother stood by and was glad. She was happy that Bambi was wild. She watched how he jumped into the air and fell again in the same spot. She understood that Bambi knew only the narrow deer tracks in the forest. He did not realize that he could move around in the open meadow.

So she came toward him, laughing, and cried, "Try to catch me." Then she was gone.

Bambi started after her. He took a few steps. Then his steps became leaps. He felt as if he were flying and he was beside himself with joy.

The swishing grass sounded wonderful to his ears. He ran around in a circle. He turned and flew off in a new circle, turned again, and kept running.

Suddenly the race was over. He came up to his mother, lifting his hoofs proudly. He looked joyfully at her. Then they walked contentedly side by side.

The wonders of the meadow amazed Bambi. Blade after blade of grass covered every inch of the ground. The meadow was starred with white daisies and golden dandelions.

Meeting Strangers

"Look," cried Bambi, "see that piece of grass jumping. Look how high it can jump!"

"That's not grass," his mother explained. "That's a nice grasshopper. He's jumping because he's afraid we'll step on him."

"Oh," said Bambi, turning to the grasshopper, "don't be afraid. We won't hurt you."

"I'm not afraid," he said, in a shaking voice. "Since it's you, it's perfectly all right. But you never know who's coming and you have to be careful."

"This is the first time in my life that I've ever been to a meadow," Bambi explained. "My mother brought me. . . ."

"That doesn't interest me at all," said the grasshopper. "I haven't time to stand here talking with you. I have to be looking for my wife." Hop! He gave a jump.

Bambi ran to his mother. "Mother, I spoke to him!" he cried.

"To whom?" his mother asked.

"To the grasshopper," Bambi said. "He was very nice. He's so wonderful and you can see through his sides."

"Those are his wings," said his mother.

"Oh," Bambi went on, "and his face is so serious and wise. And how he can jump!"

They walked on. The conversation with the grasshopper had excited Bambi. It was the first time he had ever spoken to a stranger.

Bambi noticed a bright flower moving in the tangled grasses. He looked more closely at it. It wasn't a flower, but a butterfly. Bambi crept closer.

The butterfly hung heavily to a grass stem and fanned its wings slowly.

"Please sit still," Bambi said.

"Why should I sit still? I'm a butterfly," the insect answered in surprise.

"Oh, please sit still, just for a minute," Bambi pleaded. "I've wanted so much to see you close. Please."

"Well," said the butterfly, "for your sake I will, but not for long."

Bambi stood in front of him. "How beautiful you are!" he cried. "How wonderfully beautiful like a flower!"

"What?" cried the butterfly, fanning his wings. "Did you say like a flower? In my circle it's generally thought that we're handsomer than flowers."

Bambi was embarrassed. "Oh, yes," he agreed, "much handsomer, excuse me, I only meant . . ."

"Whatever you meant is all the same to me," the butterfly replied. He arched his thin body, showing off, and played with his tiny feelers.

Bambi looked at the butterfly enchanted. "How splendid you are!" he said. "How splendid and fine! And how white your wings are!"

The beautiful butterfly spread his wings wide apart, then raised them until they folded together like an upright sail.

"Oh," cried Bambi, "I know that you are handsomer than the flowers. Besides, you can fly and the flowers can't because they grow on stems, that's why."

The butterfly spread his wings. "It's enough," he said, "that I can fly." He soared so lightly that Bambi could hardly see him or follow his flight. His wings moved gently and gracefully. Then he flew into the sunny air.

"I only sat still that long to do you a favor," he said, balancing in the air in front of Bambi. "Now I'm going."

That was how Bambi found the meadow.

Take It or Leave It

by Osmond Molarsky

One day Chester was walking past Firehouse No. 23, playing with his yoyo. He saw Linda, who was minding her own business, counting her baseball cards. "Forty-six," Linda said, when she saw Chester walking toward her.

"I'll swap you," Chester said.

"What?" Linda said.

"I'll swap you my yoyo for your baseball cards," Chester said, flicking out the yoyo and making it snap back into his hand smartly.

"I don't want to swap," Linda said. "I've got almost a full set. I need only four more."

"It's up to you," Chester said, flinging the yoyo out almost under Linda's nose. "But it's made of real boxwood."

"Real boxwood? What's that?"

"It's what they make the best yoyos out of," Chester said. "Take it or leave it."

"I'll take it," Linda said. Quick as a flash, the cards and the yoyo changed hands. Chester had the cards, and Linda had the yoyo.

"So long," Chester said, starting down the street, as Linda began to practice with the yoyo.

Chester had not gone very far when he met Pendleton on his skateboard.

"Where did you get the skateboard?" Chester asked.

"I made it," said Pendleton.

"I have almost a full set of baseball cards," Chester said. "Do you want to swap?"

"No—this is a neat skateboard."

"These are neat cards," Chester said, as he fanned them out.

"I don't know," said Pendleton, admiring the skateboard that he had built himself.

"Take it or leave it," said Chester, taking a step as if to walk away.

"I'll take it," Pendleton said, and before he knew it he was holding the cards and watching Chester speed off on his skateboard.

Chester covered quite a few blocks of the city on his new homemade skateboard. As he rolled up to the corner of Seventh and Oak, he saw an astonishing sight. It was Jiro, bouncing along on a huge rubber ball. The ball had a kind of handle at the top of it. And Jiro was bouncing along like a kangaroo.

When Jiro finally bounced to a stop, a number of people went over to look.

"What is it?" asked a man.

"It's a Kangaroo Bucking Ball," Jiro said. "You can see it on TV."

By this time, Chester had collected his wits. Rolling up to Jiro, he said, right out, "Want to swap?" He figured the best thing to do was to come right to the point.

"No," said Jiro, who had known Chester for a long time. "I'm not going to swap my Kangaroo Bucking Ball for an old homemade skateboard. You can save your breath."

"That's up to you," said Chester. "This skateboard may be homemade, but the skates are brand new." Chester started to scoot away, then made a sharp U turn and ended up exactly where he had started, in front of Jiro.

"I never saw a skateboard that could make a U turn like that," said Jiro.

"And you never will again," said Chester. "Take it or leave it."

"I'll take it."

One leap and Chester was on top of the ball and bouncing away. This was really great. This was by far the best swapping Chester had ever done. This was something he would always keep.

Chester had just made up his mind about this, when he saw a boy with a small black puppy on a string. The boy was jerking the string, and the puppy looked miserable.

"What's its name?" asked Chester.

"I don't know," said the boy, yanking on the string. "I swapped a roller skate for her."

"If she were mine, I'd call her Silky," said Chester. He would have given anything in the world, even the Kangaroo Bucking Ball, to have the puppy. But he knew he could not keep her if he brought her home. He had tried bringing puppies home twice before. But he had to get the puppy away from the boy. The boy was being mean to her.

"Did you ever ride on a Kangaroo Bucking Ball?" Chester said.

"No," said the boy.

"Do you want to try it?"

"Okay," said the boy. "Here—hold my dog."

Chester took the string. He petted the puppy, who was afraid of him at first. Then the puppy waggled up to him and licked his hand. Meanwhile, the boy leaped on the ball and bounced away for a long ride.

When the boy returned, Chester said, "Do you want to swap? I'll take your dog in trade."

"An old ball for a dog?" the boy said. "Do you think I'm crazy?"

"Here's what I can do," Chester said. "I'll throw in this lucky coin. What do you say?"

The boy had a look in his eye, as if he might ask for still something else. "I don't know," he said, yanking on the puppy's string.

"Take it or leave it," Chester said, and he started to bounce away on the ball.

"I'll take it," said the boy. "Here—take the mutt."

And that is how Chester got a dog that he could not keep and would have to swap before he went home for supper. "Come on, Silky," he said. "I've got to swap you—to some kid who likes you and who can keep you."

In the next hour, Chester tried to swap Silky for a kite with no string, for a roller skate, and for three sticks of chewing gum. The trouble was that the children did not know whether they could keep Silky or not.

By this time Chester was back in his own neighborhood. He had not gone very far past Firehouse No. 23 when whom should he see but Linda, the girl who had swapped the baseball cards for the yoyo. Linda was working the yoyo, but not very well.

"How are you doing with the yoyo?" Chester asked.

"Not so well," said Linda. "I'd just as soon swap it back for the baseball cards."

"I haven't got them," said Chester. "I swapped them for a skateboard."

"Where's the skateboard?" asked Linda.

"I swapped it for a Kangaroo Bucking Ball."

"A what? What's that?"

"One of those things. They're neat. It doesn't matter. I swapped it for Silky here."

"You sure did a lot of swapping today," said Linda.

"About average," said Chester.

"Are you through swapping for the day?" asked Linda. She was petting Silky and the dog was licking her hand.

"Why?" asked Chester.

"Would you swap Silky for this yoyo?" Linda asked.

"Will your parents let you keep her?"

"Sure."

"How do you know?" said Chester.

"They said I could have a dog for my birthday," said Linda. "Tomorrow is my birthday. We were going to the pound tomorrow to pick one out. But I'll pick Silky, right now, if you want to swap."

Chester looked at the yoyo. Looking at it one way, it was not a very good swap. A dog like Silky was worth a dozen yoyos.

"Take it or leave it," said Linda.

"I'll take it," said Chester. He gave Silky one last pat and handed her over. Linda gave him the yoyo and he put his finger through the loop in the cord. "Good-bye, Silky," he said, then turned quickly and started toward the house, flicking the yoyo out in all directions. Tomorrow, he thought, would be another day.

Robert and the Morning Things

by Hannah Ross Lurie

Greeting the morning things was the best part of Robert's day. His mistress woke very early and would open the door and let him out.

The flowers were just opening. Their green stems reached toward the sun after a quiet slumber through the peaceful darkness of the night. Dew was everywhere, feeling cool to Robert's paws.

Robert stretched, yawned, shook his furry self out, wakening his body. Although he weighed seventy pounds, when he walked his

steps were graceful. His coat was pitch black with a pure white turtleneck collar and chest. His paws were white, and his face was black, masked with a tan border and tan eyebrows. His fluffy black tail had a white tip. He looked as if an artist with a perfect hand and eye had painted him.

Although he hadn't reached his second birthday, he was full-grown and even big for his breed. He was bigger than most of the other dogs around and he knew this was because he was so well cared for.

There were other dogs out. He could smell them. Norton, the mutt, Jerome, the dachshund, and Heidi, the shepherd, all lived on his street. Their doggy scents were in the wind and floating on the air of the new day. Robert's nose began to tingle and quiver. Yes, Robert thought, as he pranced along, another day was about to begin.

There was a fat robin hopping around in the nearby bushes as Robert passed. The robin caught a worm in its beak. The robin seemed unsettled, as if it were looking for a safe spot to stand still long enough to eat the worm.

Squirrels were everywhere searching for breakfast. Puffs of smoky gray tails would appear and then zigzag around bushes and up trees. When the squirrels found a nice, fresh acorn or a delicious hickory nut, they cracked it open with their sharp white teeth. What was not munched for breakfast was stored in secret hiding places.

Robert eagerly trotted over to one of the squirrels. The squirrel immediately sensed him. He gave Robert a funny look as if he wanted to say, "We will not be provided for as you will be this winter, inside a warm home. We must plan ahead." But instead of words or a bark, the squirrel made some clicking noises and then ran up a high tree with Robert chasing close behind.

"Roberrrrrt!" His mistress's voice reached his ears. He turned on a dime, as collies know how to do, and took off toward home. There was the bright face of his mistress by the door waiting for him. He looked up at her. His heart was full of love, and he smiled.

Jenny petted the soft fur on the top of his head and gently scratched his ears. "Good morning, Robert," she said.

"She is always right," thought Robert. "It is a good morning."

Jenny and Robert at the Seashore

by Hannah Ross Lurie

The first rays of golden sunlight peeked through the window touching warmly on Robert's furry coat, reminding him to awaken and begin the morning.

Robert padded lightly into the next room and nuzzled his sleeping mistress's face with his nose.

"I'm glad you woke me early," she said.

"We're going on an adventure. We're going crabbing." She let him out the front door. "Stay outside till I'm ready."

Within a few minutes, Jenny, Robert's mistress, had put on her bathing suit, made her bed, filled Robert's empty water bowl, and eaten her breakfast.

She opened the door and found Robert sniffing around in the garden. Robert was enjoying the seashore smells. Jenny walked out of the cottage and went to get her bike. In the basket she put a long-handled net and a bucket with heavy string, meat for bait, and a knife.

Robert ran alongside his mistress as she rode her bike down the street. Jenny came to a stoplight. "Stay!" Jenny commanded. "Sit," she said. In a few minutes the light changed. "Come, Robert," ordered Jenny.

At the end of the street was a wooden dock. Beyond the dock lay a stretch of water, free air, and open space—swept only by the winds and wings of birds. On both sides of the dock there were boats tied up, rocking gently in the water. Tall posts were in the water. The posts supported the dock. At the top of each post sat one large sea gull.

"This is the bay, Robert. It is different from the ocean. Do you like it?" Jenny hugged him. Robert cautiously peeked over the side into the water. It was smooth and calm.

"Now sit here and bring me luck," said Jenny. "Mrs. Sprague, our neighbor on the corner, is going to pay me fifty cents for every crab I catch. I could sure use the money when they have the book sale in the fall."

The air was clean and wet with salt spray. Robert knew he liked it here. It was cool by the water. He had done a lot of summer shedding, but his coat was still heavy and hot. Robert peeked again over the side and watched a school of silver minnows playing in the water.

Robert licked his chops as he watched Jenny tie a chunk of meat on a string. She dropped it over the side and into the water. The splash made the minnows dart away. Jenny tied the string to a post. "Now, we have to gather seaweed to line our pail, so the crabs we catch will stay fresh until we go home." It was high tide on the bay; Jenny only had to reach down from the dock to pick up a clump of floating seaweed. She then carefully lined the bucket with it.

"Now," she said, "let's play, and we will check our line from time to time."

She stepped aboard one of the open boats tied to the dock. It was Mrs. Sprague's boat. She had given Jenny permission to play in it if she promised to be careful.

Jenny went right to the captain's wheel. She steered, pretending to give Robert a ride out on the bay. Then she decided it was time to check her crab line. She and Robert jumped out onto the dock.

It was a good day for crabbing. Jenny slowly pulled up her line, and there on the end was a large blue crab. She carefully dipped her net under it, then set the net down on the dock. Jenny picked up the crab by one leg and dropped it into the bucket. Once a crab fell back into the water as Jenny was pulling up the string. This made her laugh aloud. When she caught a crab that was not full size she would throw it back and the crab would swim away and disappear. She now kept busy baiting and watching her line. Almost every time she lifted her line there would be another crab or two. Soon she had a bucket full of crabs.

Once, a baby blowfish mistakenly swam into her net as she reached down for a crab. The blowfish blew itself up into a balloon. Jenny picked up the "balloon" gently and tossed it back into the water.

All of this activity attracted the attention of the large gulls. The gulls left their posts and seemed to be fluttering and squawking everywhere, sometimes diving too close to Jenny. When they became that bold, Robert would bark at them and they would flap off, making strange noises and calls. There were different kinds of gulls, and they all made different sounds. Some called, "Kleew, kleew, kleew." Some called a high "Whee-ee." And others said, "Kah, kah, kah."

Robert Goes Visiting

At the far end of the dock a group of children were fishing. They were noisy, and a lot of pails and rods were lying on the dock. Some of the children slowly started to drift toward Jenny. "Oh, look at all the crabs in this bucket," called someone, and some of the children crowded around and peered into Jenny's bucket of live crabs.

Robert began testing Jenny. He would take a few steps, stop, turn around, and then look at her. Jenny knew he wanted to visit the other children. "Okay, you may go," she said, "but you must come back when I call you." He started walking toward the children that were still at the end of the dock. Jenny continued dropping her line into the water, thinking of all the good books she could buy with the money she would earn today.

The air was suddenly filled with alarm and noise. Children were excitedly yelling, the gulls began screeching and squawking, but loudest of all was Robert. His bark was heard above everything. Jenny knew that bark. It meant trouble. Robert needed help. Children

were running back and forth on the dock, waving their arms. No one knew what to do. In the commotion and excitement, Jenny's bucket of crabs was knocked over. Crabs were scurrying everywhere, falling and plopping back into the water. Plop! Plop! Every crab that had been in the bucket quickly scampered around on the dock in every direction and then over the side. Jenny had no time to pick them up. She had to see why Robert was barking!

There at the end of the dock was a boy holding on to his fishing rod, and on the end of the line wriggling desperately was a strange creature. The boy, not knowing what to do, was afraid to let go, and afraid not to let go. Jenny

called out as she ran toward the excitement, "It's an oyster cracker!" She had recognized it right away. The fish had been hooked by the gill and its wide jaw was free and dangerous. The fish now lay on the dock snapping at everyone. Each snap made the children scream louder.

Jenny knew the power of that fierce set of jaws. They were a monster's jaws, containing double rows of teeth like a shark's. Blunt, heavy teeth able to crush the hard shells of oysters could also rip open a child's hand. The terror of the moment seemed to touch all things—the screeching gulls, the barking Robert, and the excited, frightened children.

Jenny soon spotted the boy's fishing knife on the dock and quickly picked it up and cut his line. She then picked up the cut line and quickly threw the snapping fish back into the bay. Splash! As the oyster cracker hit the water, the children let out a cheer.

Jenny returned to her spot on the dock where her empty bucket was lying. There were no crabs. They were all gone.

The sun, looking like a big orange ball, was still up there in the sky, and there were still some hours before dark. Without the trouble, Jenny and Robert would have been ready to leave. She put the seaweed back in the bucket.

Then she cut a new piece of bait, tied it on her string, and dropped it back into the water.

"That's the way it is, Robert. Plans do not always work out perfectly. But we had the fun of catching that first bunch of crabs—now perhaps they will all come back for a second try at the bait. They are still hungry. In fact, they must be hungrier than ever. And I doubt that they remember how they were caught the first time."

Robert was glad to go on with the fun.

HOW TO FLY

The Flying Festoon

Oh I'm going to ride on The Flying Festoon—
I'll jump on his back and I'll whistle a tune,
And we'll fly to the outermost tip of the moon,
The Flying Festoon and I.

I'm taking a sandwich, and ball and a prune,
And we're leaving this evening precisely at noon,
For I'm going to fly with The Flying Festoon . . .
Just as soon as he learns how to fly.

—Shel Silverstein

Boats Sail on the Rivers

Boats sail on the rivers,
  And ships sail on the seas;
But clouds that sail across the sky
  Are prettier far than these.
There are bridges on the rivers,
  As pretty as you please;
But the bow that bridges heaven,
  And overtops the trees,
And builds a road from earth to sky,
  Is prettier far than these.

—Christina Rossetti

UNIT TWO

Times Past

Abe Lincoln and the Borrowed Book

by Charles C. Walcutt

Tall, lanky Abe Lincoln hurried through the forest. He could not wait to reach home. The cold wind pinched his face, and the sun had almost set in the west. At night, the trees in the forest looked like cruel, tall pirates guarding the forest's green treasures. Abe was not afraid of the woods at night, for he had lived most of his life in the western wilderness. But it was much nicer, just the same, to be home in the log cabin with his family, in front of the warm fireplace.

The wind was growing stronger, and it was getting harder and harder to walk. In his hand, the boy tightly held the book that had caused him to stay out so late. Eleven-year-old Abe could not lose this book. He had walked more than three miles to borrow it. The wind was blowing so fiercely now that it almost snatched the book from his hand.

Abe had tried for months to persuade Mr. Crawford to lend him this book, and the old man had finally agreed. It was one of the few books owned by Pigeon Creek settlers, for not many of them could read, and books were very rare in the wilderness.

Abe walked faster and faster, hunching his shoulders to keep the wind from his long neck. He was getting closer to home, and he was so hungry that he thought he could smell the roast he knew his mother was cooking for dinner. The cabin now appeared in the distance, through the trees. Soon Abe could see the two windows, dimly lighted. They were just narrow slits in the logs, covered with pieces of greased paper which kept out some of the cold and let in a little light. They were not nearly so good as glass, but they did not have glass in the wilderness.

Now Abe could see smoke coming from the chimney. "After dinner," he thought, as he came up to the door, "I'll begin to read my book. I hope I can finish it before the end of the week."

He slowly opened the door. It squeaked, and a sudden gust of wind followed him into the cabin.

"Abe, is that you?" a voice called from another room. "Hurry up and shut the door."

Abe closed the door. "I'm sorry I'm so late, Mother. Mr. Crawford still did not want to give me the book. But Mrs. Crawford persuaded him to keep his promise." Abe took off his woolen scarf, beaver hat, and bearskin coat. He put them on the shelf in the cupboard and laid his book on one of the three-legged stools by the big table.

"What's the book about, Son?" Mr. Lincoln asked. He knew that Abe would do anything for a book, no matter what it was about, for the boy liked to read more than anything else. No matter what he was doing—cutting trees, tending cattle, building a fire—his mind was always on books. Abe was not lazy when he was interested in something, but none of the neighbors liked to have him work for them, for his mind was never on his work. So he seemed lazy to them.

"The book is about the life of Washington," Abe answered. "The name sounds familiar, but I'm not quite sure where I've heard it before."

Mother laughed, "Oh, Abe, I'm sure you know of Washington. Haven't you ever talked about him in school?"

"No, Mother, we've been studying about Columbus, and we've learned how to add numbers and how to write, but we've never talked about any Mr. Washington."

"Son, haven't you ever learned that George Washington was the first president of our country?" Mr. Lincoln asked.

"What's a president?" asked one of Abe's younger sisters.

"He leads the government of the country," Abe proudly answered. "Now I know where I've heard of him. We've talked about George Washington quite a bit down at the general store. I've seen several old newspapers with stories about him. It's going to be fun to learn all about his life at last."

Mr. and Mrs. Lincoln smiled at each other. They were proud of their son. He was rapidly becoming one of the best students in the Pigeon Creek settlement. There were still many things the boy did not know, for books were very hard to find in the wilderness settlement. But Abe read whenever he could and he learned more and more each day.

Work and Study

When dinner was over, the family helped Mrs. Lincoln clean the dishes and put them back on the wall shelf. Then the three girls, John, and Abe stretched out on the bear rug in front of the glowing fireplace. After dinner, the family always sat near the fire and talked. Then each would get something he or she liked to do. The house would become completely silent, except for the crackling of the fire.

Once the after-dinner talk was over, the three girls brought their sewing over to the fire and Mrs. Lincoln began her knitting. Mr. Lincoln and John began to fix one of the three-legged stools that had become shaky. Abe picked up his book and eagerly began to read it.

Soon the family made a quiet picture. There in front of the fire, everyone was warm and safe and happy. Abe was stretched out on his stomach with his head near the fire, reading. The girls were by his feet. Mother sat on one of the stools with her long wooden knitting needles and dark gray wool, and Father and

John were busily whittling a new leg for the shaky stool.

Abe was lost in his book. He had heard people talk about the early days of his country, but he had never been able to read about them. He read slowly, for he did not want to forget a single word, and turned the pages carefully, for the book was old and the pages would easily tear.

Outside, it had begun to rain. The drops thumped softly on the wooden roof of the cabin. Abe felt a drop hit him on the head.

"A new leak!" he exclaimed.

"Get a bucket to put under it," his father advised. "We'll fix it tomorrow."

Every time it rained, water would leak through cracks between the logs. The family could never tell where a new leak would come. Sometimes they would wake up to find some valued possession soaking wet.

"It's time for bed, children," said Mother.

John and the girls put their work away. But Abe asked, "May I stay up to read just a little longer?"

"No, Son," answered his father. "You must get up early, remember."

Abe knew that he should obey his father, but he longed to finish the page he had been

reading. Then he had an idea. Instead of putting the book away, he would read it by candlelight in the loft. Abe quietly lit a candle in the fireplace and climbed up the pegs to his bed.

Up in the loft, Abe felt cozy. He put the candle and the book down on the small shelf near his bed and undressed. He could hear the rain drumming on the roof above him. He took the book and began to read again. As he read, his eyelids began to droop. Close by he could hear the thump of rain on wood. He blew out the candle and tossed his book on the little shelf near his bed. "There must be a new leak up here," he thought to himself. "I should see where it is, but . . . it . . . will . . . wait . . . for . . . morn . . . ing," and he dropped off to sleep.

The next morning Abe got up before dawn, dressed, and climbed down from the loft. He planned to restock the woodpile. As he stepped outside, his feet sank into the wet, muddy earth. "It must have been a bad rainstorm last night," Abe said to himself. "This mud is almost three inches deep."

Terrible Trouble

Abe brought a pile of wood into the house and began a fire. Then he remembered his book and decided to take it outside with him to read until Mother had breakfast ready. He climbed back up to the loft. "Now where did I leave it?" he wondered. Then he remembered the leak he had heard last night. "I'd better see if I can find it this morning, so that Father can fix it before anything is ruined."

It was still dark in the loft and difficult to see. As Abe felt around, his hand touched something wet and soggy. "Oh, the leak must have been here over the shelf," he realized, "and something has already been ruined. I just hope it isn't anything important."

Abe took the soggy something into his hand and climbed back down the ladder to the fire. Abe had forgotten the new book and just wanted to see what had been ruined. He had only two books of his own on the shelf and one writing book. "Which of these was it," he wondered, and he wished he had paid attention to the leak last night. "I could have taken all my things from the shelf."

As Abe neared the fire, he could see the damaged cover of the book. "Oh, it can't be, it just can't be!" Abe said aloud. His voice echoed through the still house. In his hand he held a wet, ruined copy of *The Life of Washington.*

"Abe, what is the matter?" his mother asked. His cry had awakened her.

"Look at this, look at this!" Abe exclaimed, almost in tears. He was not one to cry at trifles, but this was terrible.

Abe's mother looked at the soggy book and realized why her son was so unhappy.

"What will I do, Mother?" Abe asked.

"You'll have to take it to Mr. Crawford and explain how it happened," his mother replied.

Abe knew that he would not be able to eat anything that morning; so he asked, "May I leave now, Mother, before breakfast?"

Mrs. Lincoln, seeing her son's unhappiness, agreed. "But the Crawfords won't be up this early," she said.

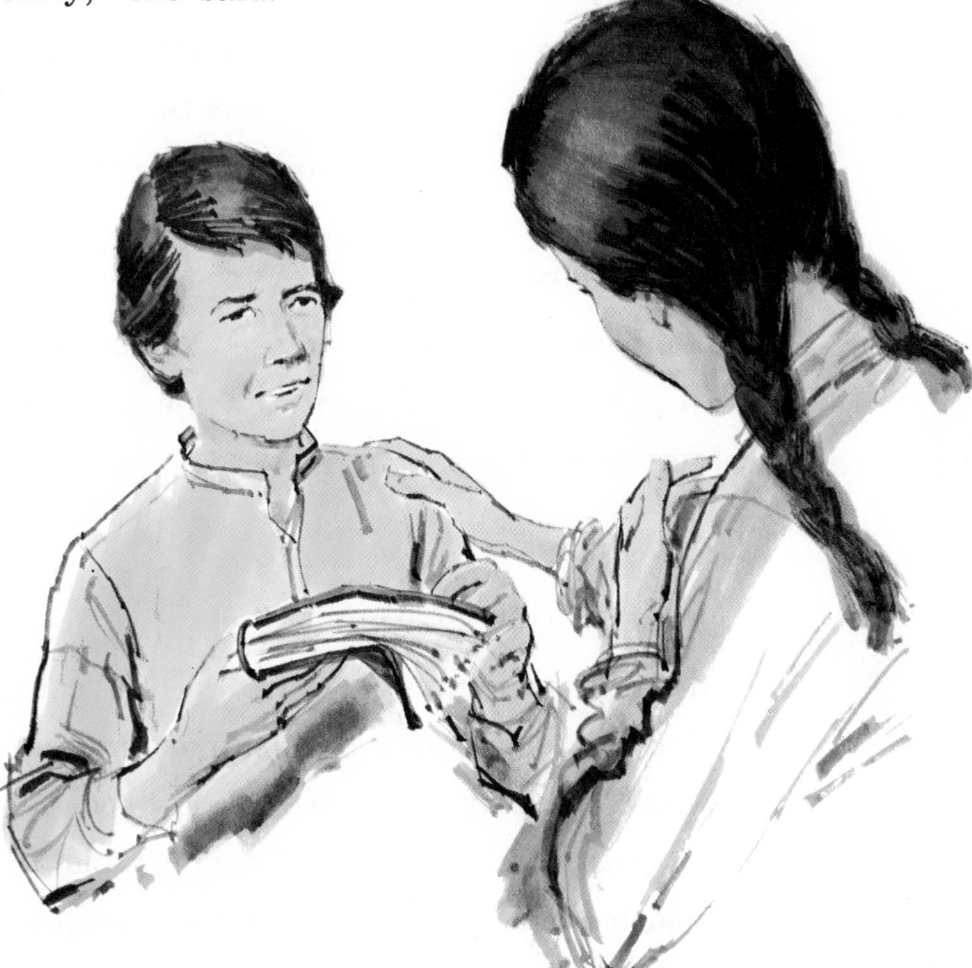

"It will take me almost an hour to get over there, and by that time they should be almost finished with breakfast."

"All right, Son. Good luck!"

As Abe walked, the fear grew stronger. "What will he do to me?" he wondered. "I deserve any punishment he decides on, but he can be so mean. Why wasn't I careful with it?"

At last, he saw the smoke from the cabin rising in the distance. There was the clearing where the Crawfords had built their cabin. "I'd better wait a little while, until I'm sure he's finished with breakfast," Abe thought. He remembered his mother's advice, "Always wait until people have finished their meals before asking them for anything."

Helped by a Friend

Abe sat down on a log in front of the cabin door. He was trembling. In just a few minutes he would be facing Mr. Crawford. The book felt like a knife that was digging into his hand. He wished he could throw it high over the trees and run home.

When Abe could no longer stand the waiting, he timidly knocked at the cabin door.

He heard footsteps inside the cabin. The door slowly opened. Mrs. Crawford saw the face of a frightened boy.

"Good morning, Abe," she said. "What brings you here so early?"

Abe opened his mouth, but no sound came out. He had lost his voice. All he could do was hold up the soggy book. Mrs. Crawford took it from Abe. "Oh, Abe," she said.

From inside the cabin Abe heard a harsh voice growl, "Who is it?"

Mrs. Crawford led Abe into the room. At the table, her husband was finishing his breakfast.

"What is he doing here this early?" he demanded.

Abe was shaking.

Mrs. Crawford held out the book and showed it to her husband.

"What . . ." the old man shouted. "How did this happen, you careless boy?" He got up from the table.

Abe still could not talk. He just stood there trembling in front of Mr. Crawford.

"You'll pay for this, just wait," the old man threatened. "You should have been more careful."

Mrs. Crawford went over to her husband and tried to calm him down.

"Now the boy didn't mean it. Don't be hard on him," she pleaded.

"Abe, you'd better leave now, but come back this evening. You will have to do something to pay for the book, but I'll try to get my husband to agree to something reasonable," said Mrs. Crawford. She led Abe to the door.

Abe walked on to the schoolhouse. He was already late, but nothing mattered now. He felt as if it were the end of the world.

That evening, after school was over, he sadly walked back to the Crawford cabin. "What will happen to me?" he wondered.

After knocking on the door, he was led into the cabin by the kind Mrs. Crawford. She looked serious, but she was still gentle. Abe took a deep breath and followed her. Mr.

Crawford sat near the fire, with the damaged book in his hands. Abe stayed as far away from him as the size of the cabin would allow.

"I've decided on your punishment," he growled. "You will have to pay me seventy-five cents for the book."

Abe was shocked. "Where can I earn seventy-five cents?" he asked.

"I've already thought about that," Mr. Crawford went on. "If you feed and tend the settlement's cows in the pasture, and watch for thieves and wild animals all day, the settlers will pay you twenty-five cents a day. You must work from the rising to the setting of the sun. In three days, you can earn enough money to pay me."

Then Mrs. Crawford came over to Abe and said, "Abe, after you have paid us for the book, we will buy a new one. Then I may be able to get my husband to let you keep the old one."

Abe smiled. He was very happy. He would have to work to pay for his carelessness, but the book about the great president would be his forever.

Abe continued to study. In a few years he became one of the most hard-working and learned people in the state of Illinois. And, one day, he would become a great president himself.

Both in summer and winter
we used to move a lot.
Felt pen, 1970

Pitseolak: Pictures out of My Life

from recorded interviews by Dorothy Eber

My name is Pitseolak, the Eskimo word for the sea pigeon. When I see pitseolaks over the sea, I say, "There go those lovely birds—that's me, flying!"

I became an artist to earn money, but I think I am a real artist. I draw the old ways, the things we did long ago. I don't know how many drawings I have done but more than a thousand.

I have lost the time when I was born, but I am old now—my sons say maybe I am 70. I was born on Nottingham Island in Hudson's Bay. Timungiak was my mother; Ottochie was my father. I had a happy childhood. I was always healthy. We had a large family—three boys and two girls—and we were always happy to be together.

We lived in the old Eskimo way. We would pick up and go to different camps. We were free to move anywhere, and we lived in many camps. Sometimes they were near Cape Dorset and sometimes they were far away.

When we were children we played lots of make-believe. We used to play igloo. We used to play dog-team.

Sometimes in the winter it was boring in the igloo, but we never stayed inside much. We had warmer clothes in those days, and it used to be fun when it was windy. We had toy sleds and we played outside most of the day. Now children are in school all day and often stay indoors.

I don't remember how old I was when I married, but girls got married very young then. Now they are older. Ashoona and I were married in the summer on Cape Dorset.

In the old days we had different kinds of housing for the different seasons. We had the igloo, the *kaamuk,* which is a tent-hut, and the sealskin summer tents.

We played lots of games. One game was the Eskimo tennis! We threw a ball underhand and tried to catch it in a sealskin racket. We made the ball from caribou skin and stuffed it with something. We used to play this game a lot, even in winter. It was a good game, but they don't play it now.

This is how we played tennis.
Felt pen, 1970

Very often in those days when we felt happy in camp, Ashoona and I would play the accordion. The little children would come and dance.

At Natsilik, my husband died. He died of a very bad sickness. Many people died at that time in the camps.

After Ashoona died, we were very poor and we needed to make some money. One day I heard that a man in the government office was asking for drawings. His name was Jim Houston. Many people were already making drawings to earn money.

I wanted to do drawings, too. I bought some paper myself and I think I made four small drawings. I meant the drawings to be animals, but they turned out to be funny-looking because I had never done drawings before. I took these drawings to Jim's office. He gave me some money. I think it was $20. Jim told me to draw the old ways, and I've been drawing them ever since.

Does it take much planning to draw? *Ahalona!* It takes much thinking, and it is hard to think. It is hard like housework.

One day I drew an Eskimo woman with a blue-fish spear. I did not want to leave the spear alone; that is why I put the bird on her head. There's a baby hidden inside the parka, too —you can tell by the shape of the parka!

The woman with the blue-fish spear. Felt pen, 1970

To make prints is not easy. But I am happy doing the prints. After my husband died, I felt very alone and unwanted. Making prints is what has made me happiest since he died.

Now we have a Co-op here on Cape Dorset. The Co-op sends carvings and prints to the south, and it is owned by Eskimos. We get artist's papers and pens from the Co-op.

Since the Co-op began, I have earned a lot of money with my drawings. I am happy to have the money and I am glad we have a Co-op.

Sometimes, when I see pictures of my drawings in books, I laugh. I laugh to think they have become something. But even when they are waiting for paper from the south, the Co-op gives some to me. Sometimes I am the only one who is given artist's paper. I feel sorry when other people don't have paper—paper which I can get.

I know I have had an unusual life, being born in a skin tent and living to hear that two men have landed on the moon. I think the new times started for Eskimos when new people came from southern Canada to the Arctic. They began to build houses, and they helped us to get these houses. That's why life changed.

Today I like living in a house that is always warm. But sometimes I want to move and go to the camps where I have been. The old life was hard, but it was good. It was happy.

I have heard that they like my drawings in the south and I am grateful and happy about it. I am going to keep on making prints until they tell me to stop. If no one tells me to stop, I shall make them as long as I am well.

My son Kumwartok wants me to do some drawings to put around the house. But I think I will do some and take them to the Co-op.

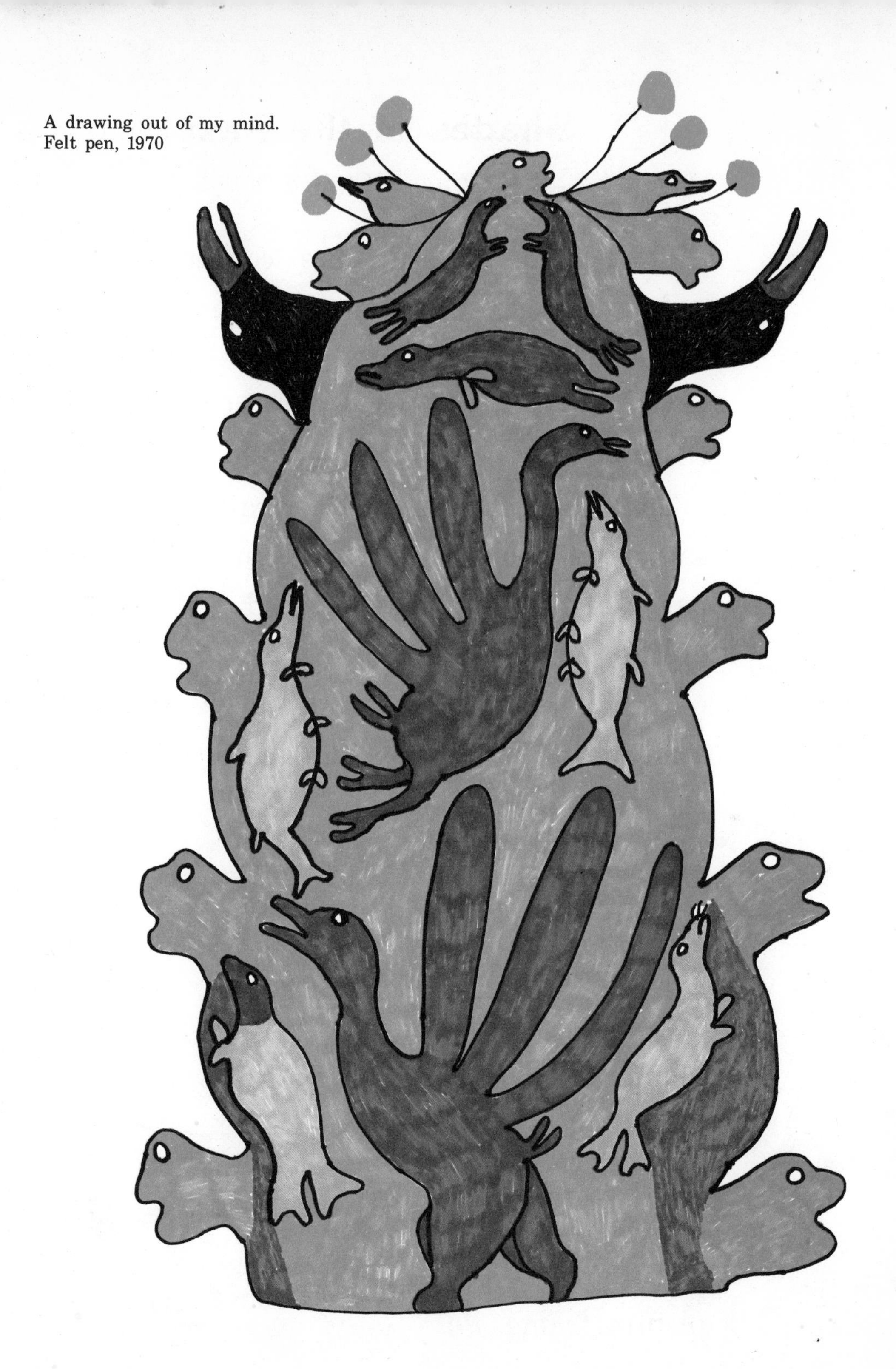

A drawing out of my mind.
Felt pen, 1970

Shades of the Past

by Cheryl G. Hoople

Long before there were country stores, peddlers once traveled across America's back roads, selling their wares. All were welcome, but children saved their heartiest hurrahs for the shademaker.

The shademaker made portraits. A person sat between a lighted candle and a piece of paper. The shademaker traced the person's profile, or silhouette, on paper.

You, too, can be a shademaker. Just ask someone to sit for you and start tracing!

Materials:

tape
2 large sheets of paper
  (1 white, 1 dark)
blank wall with a smooth surface
flashlight
sharp pencil
scissors
white glue
picture frame

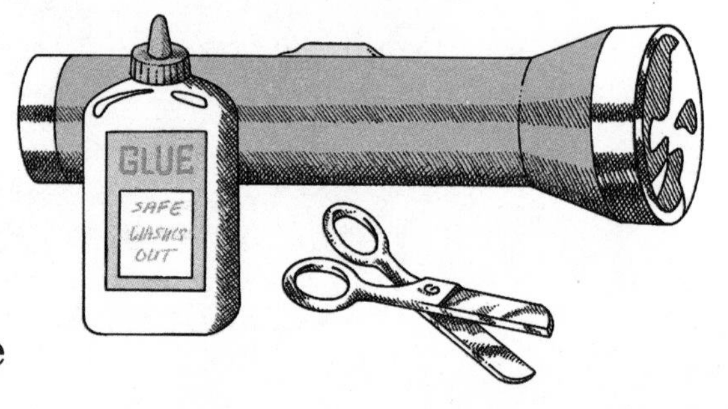

1. Tape a sheet of white paper to the wall.

2. Place the person between the flashlight and the paper. You can rest the flashlight on a table, on top of some books. Move the person or the flashlight backward or forward so that the silhouette fits your paper. Turn the person's head until the profile is sharp and clear.

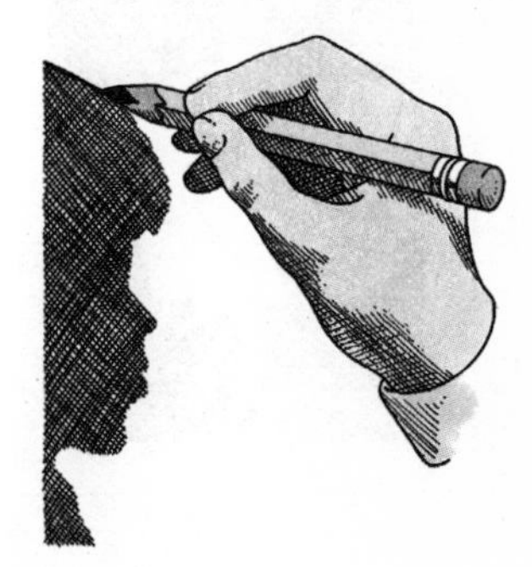

3. Do your tracing in a darkened room where there is only one light source—your flashlight. Carefully trace around the profile. Be sure to include wisps of hair, wrinkles, and the neckline.

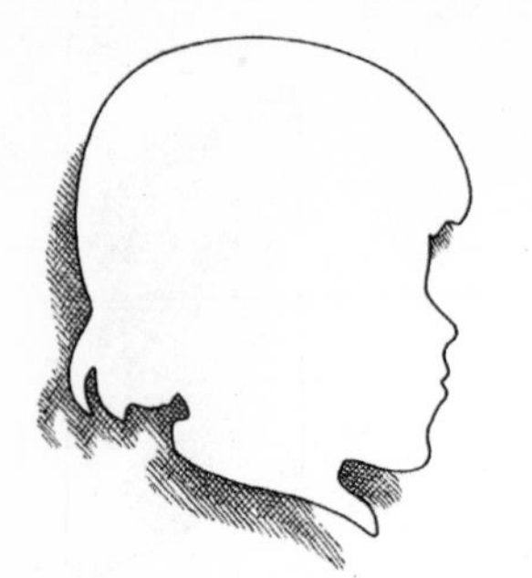

4. Cut out the silhouette and glue it to a second sheet of paper. You could also cut out all the paper *within* the silhouette and place this "hollow-cut" *over* the second sheet of paper.

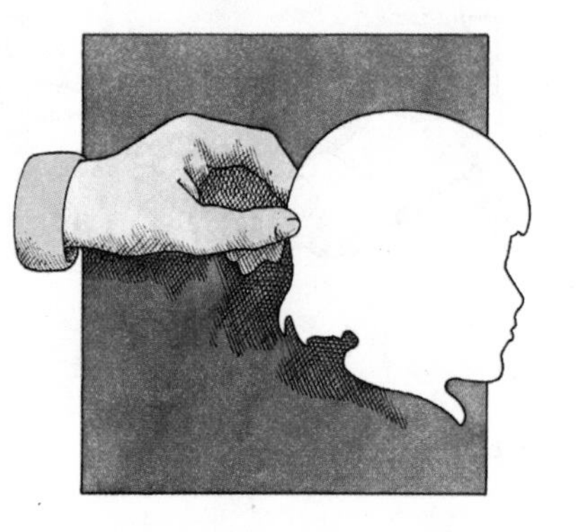

5. Select a picture frame or make a frame with poster cardboard. Use your silhouette on stationery or greeting cards. Try silhouettes of your family and friends, or even your pet—if it will hold still!

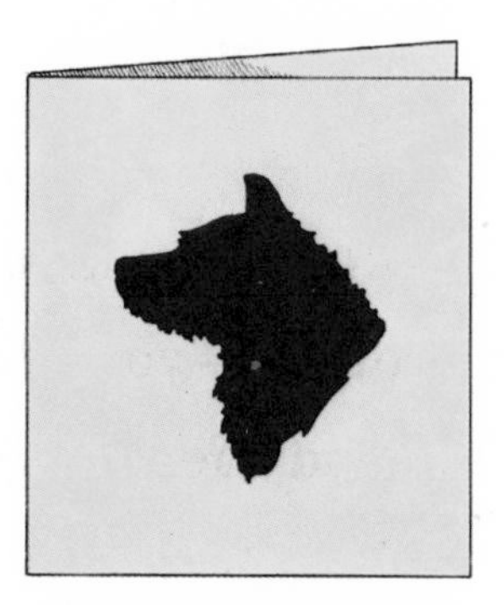

Camels Come to America

by Laura Jehn Menides

In the 1840s, Kit Carson and two other scouts went on a long trip. They explored the new, vast territory in the southwest of America. Few people lived on the land they traveled over. It was a wilderness of rocks and hills and dust and heat. It was very dangerous for people who did not know their way.

Kit and his men rode their horses over the dry, stony soil. They traveled through the hot deserts in Arizona and California. It was a rough, hard trip for the horses. The animals had to carry heavy packs. There was practically no water for them. And there were few plants and little grass to feed them. The horses always grew tired quickly in the hot sun. Because they were tired, the pace was very slow.

A thought came to Kit Carson and the other scouts. There were deserts in other parts of the world. What did the people in other countries do to cross the hot, sandy land?

"Camels! That was the answer," said the scouts. The biggest problem in the desert was the lack of water, and camels could go for a long time without water, much longer than horses or mules.

Kit Carson and his friends were not the only people who thought of bringing camels to America. Other scouts and mail carriers and explorers thought of it too.

Soon the United States Army decided to test the camels. They decided to bring a few camels from Africa to see whether they really were better than horses and mules in the desert.

The Army sent two men, Henry Wayne and David Porter, across the ocean to buy the camels. About a year later, the men returned from their trip with thirty-six camels.

What a strange sight it must have been! A caravan of big camels traveling toward the Army base! The camels were so strange and new in America that even the horses and mules became frightened at the sight of them. The horses would turn the wagons upside down. Of course, the American horsemen and muleteers did not like to see their animals frightened, and they blamed the camels. They did not believe that the camels could do a better job than their horses and mules. Wayne had to show the American horse and mule men how valuable the camels were. He thought up a fine demonstration.

Wayne's Demonstration

At the Army base, Wayne gathered together all the men who disliked the camels. He led his best camel to stand before them. Then he made the camel kneel, and he loaded two big bales of hay on its back. The muleteers started to shout, "It will never lift the load. It will never do it." They knew that their mules could only carry one of those bales, never two of them.

Wayne paused a while. When the crowd of men became quiet again, he loaded two more bales of hay on the camel's back. "Four bales," shouted the men. "No animal can lift that much weight."

Wayne ordered the camel to get up. Much to the surprise of the men, the camel got up and started to walk away carrying the four big bales.

The men had to cheer for the strange animal. Even though they did not like the camel, they had to admit that it was a useful animal.

Wayne and Porter made more trips across the ocean to buy camels. Soon it was a pretty common sight to see an Army camel carrying the mail between towns in the Southwest.

Wayne and Porter and another man named Beale discovered that on rocky land, three camels could carry the same load that six horses or mules could pull in a wagon. The camels could travel almost twice as fast too.

At first, then, the Army experiment was very successful. When there was a long trip to make over a desert with no water or plants, the camel could make it easily. Beale and Wayne discovered that camels could travel two, three, four, five, or even six days without water. Moreover, when the desert got cold at night, the men would gather around the camels to keep themselves warm.

Once the Army decided to put the camels to a real test. A team of camels and a team of mules would be sent on a sixty-mile trip over a frontier road. The camels and the mules would have to carry the same load.

Carrying one load were twelve mules and two wagons. Carrying another load were six camels. Would the camels or the mules win, the Army men wanted to know.

Much to their surprise, the camels made the trip in two and a half days, while it took the mules four days.

Even in the rain and mud on rough roads, a team of camels could beat a wagon pulled by horses.

Beale and Wayne discovered other good things about camels. The animal needed very little food on its trips. It grazed on almost every plant that grew, including the thistle. The camel could be used to carry loads from the time it was four years old until it was twenty-five. A strong camel could carry 450 to 600 pounds and travel all day long with practically no rest.

The Reason for Failure

Why was the Army experiment a failure? There were two reasons. First, the camel had a thick, leathery sole on its foot. In its native land, the sands of the desert did not bother its feet. The sharp stones in the dry American deserts cut its soles so badly that it made it impossible for it to walk after a while.

The second reason is more important. The American mule drivers and horse riders could not get used to the camels. They tried to treat the camels as they treated their mules and horses. They did not learn that you cannot treat a camel roughly.

One of the Army muleteers kicked a camel that would not get up. The animal spat at the muleteer. The man grew even angrier. He threatened the camel with a stick. At this the camel let out a scream. It defended itself by biting the man's arm.

From then on, practically all the muleteers and horsemen disliked the camels. Beale tried to explain how to handle the camels, but the Army muleteers would not listen.

Many of the animals died of thirst simply because the Army muleteers did not know enough about them. The men would not give the camel water as long as its hump was big, because they thought that the camel stored water in its hump. We now know, of course, that this is not true. Camels can go for long periods without water, not because they store it in their humps, but because they can stand a great deal of dryness.

Beale found out that while the camels could go without water for up to six days, they would ordinarily drink about every two days.

When the Army entered the war between the North and the South and Beale was sent North, the Army experiment with camels came to an end.

What happened to the camels? Many of the animals were set free and they became wild in the desert. Others were sold to zoos and circuses and parks. One man bought a team of camels and held an exciting camel race.

Beale, who was now General Beale, bought a team of camels when the war was over. He used them to make long trips and to construct roads near his ranch.

Some of the camels were sold to mining companies, and they were used to haul big loads of salt and coal and other minerals. But again, the miners did not know how to treat the animals. They were frightened at the strange roar the camels made when they tried to treat them like horses. This experiment also ended in failure, and the animals were sold or set free.

What happened to the camels that were set free? They strayed to the open ranges and became wild in the desert. Every once in a while a man looking for gold would see a wild camel running across a prairie. But as the years passed, the camels became more and more scarce. The last camel, it seems, was spotted in 1913.

Americans must now go to zoos to see the animal that once roamed our land.

Facts about Camels

by Laura Jehn Menides

Kinds of camels: There are two kinds of camels. One is the Arabian camel. It has one large hump on its back. Some Arabian camels are raised for riding and racing.

The other kind is the Bactrian camel from Asia. It has two humps on its back. It is stronger than the Arabian camel. Both kinds were brought to America.

Ability to go without water: A camel can go for days, or even months, without water. One reason is that a camel can stand a great deal of dryness.

Another reason is that the body temperature of the camel varies with the weather. On a very hot day, the camel's temperature rises. It does not sweat as much as other animals. For this reason, its body does not lose water quickly.

Body temperature: On cold nights, the camel's temperature lowers itself. Then the camel gives off heat. This is why travelers will keep close to their camels on cold nights.

The hump: The hump is a large lump of fat. On a long trip, the camel can absorb some of the fatty lump into its body for food. Sometimes after a long, hard trip the hump is almost flat. It can even slip down to the camel's side.

The Storyteller

Nowadays, we sit around
And read or watch TV,
Or listen to the radio
Or choose a movie to see.

But long ago, a Storyteller
Would go from town to town.
The people loved to see him come;
They'd quickly gather 'round.

All hushed, they'd listen silently
To the stories being told:
Of kings and queens, of tribal chiefs,
Of battlefields of old.

I'm glad I'm here in modern days;
I'm not an old-time dweller.
But once, just once, I'd like to hear
The old-time Storyteller.

—Peg Chagnon

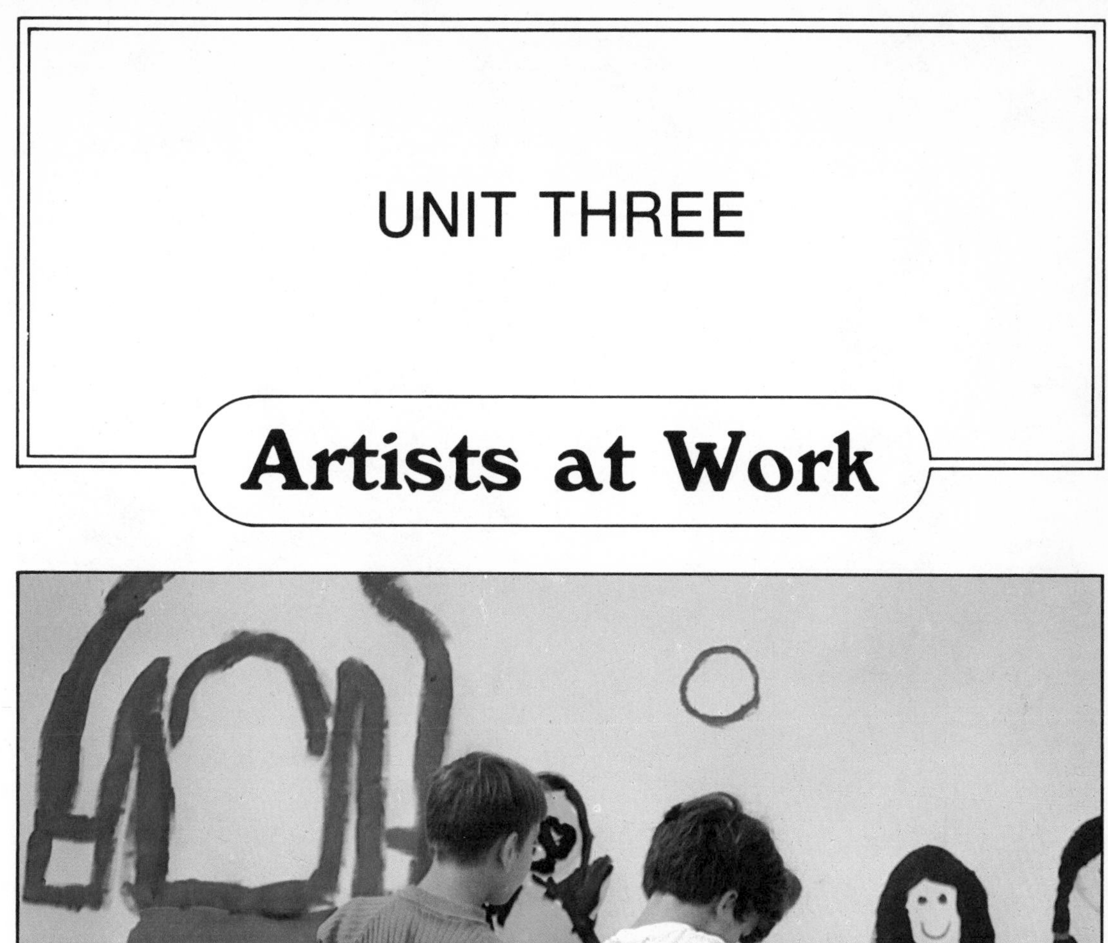

UNIT THREE

Artists at Work

Frederick

by Leo Lionni

All along the meadow there was an old stone wall. In that wall, not far from the barn, a family of field mice had their home.

The farmers had moved away and the barn was empty. Since winter was not far off, the little mice began to gather corn and nuts and wheat and straw. They all worked day and night—all except Frederick.

"Frederick, why don't you work?" they asked.

"I *do* work," said Frederick. "I gather sun rays for the cold dark winter days."

Later, they saw Frederick sitting there, staring at the meadow. They said, "And now, Frederick?" "I gather colors," he answered, "for winter is gray."

And once Frederick seemed half-asleep. "Are you dreaming, Frederick?" they asked.

But he said, "Oh, no, I am gathering words. The winter days are long and many, and we'll run out of things to say."

The winter days came, and the first snow fell. The five little mice took to their hideout in the stones.

At first there was lots to eat. The mice told stories of foolish foxes and silly cats. They were a happy family.

But little by little they had nibbled up most of the nuts, the straw, and the corn. It was cold in the wall and no one felt like talking.

Then they remembered what Frederick had said about sun rays and colors and words.

"What about *your* supplies, Frederick?" they asked.

"Close your eyes," said Frederick, as he climbed on a big stone. "Now I send you the rays of the sun. Do you feel how their golden glow . . ." And as Frederick spoke of the sun the four little mice began to feel warmer. Was it Frederick's voice? Was it magic?

"And how about the colors, Frederick?" they asked eagerly.

"Close your eyes again," Frederick said. Then he told them of the blue periwinkles, the red poppies in the yellow wheat, and the green leaves of the berry bush. They saw the colors as clearly as if they had been painted in their minds.

"And the words, Frederick?"

Frederick cleared his throat, waited a moment, and then, as if from a stage, he said:
"Who scatters snowflakes? Who melts the ice?
Who spoils the weather? Who makes it nice?

Who grows the four-leaf clovers in June?
Who dims the daylight? Who lights the moon?
Four little field mice who live in the sky.
Four little field mice . . . way up high.
One is the Springmouse who turns on the showers.
Then comes the Summer who paints in the flowers.
The Fallmouse is next with walnuts and wheat.
And Winter is last . . . with little cold feet.
Aren't we lucky the seasons are four?
Think of a year with one less . . . or one more!"

When Frederick had finished, they applauded.

"But Frederick," they said, "you are a poet!"

Frederick blushed and said shyly, "I know it."

Thalia Brown and the Blue Bug

by Michelle Dionetti

Grandma Brown holds the baby. He is small and brown against her big white jacket. Dad is talking to James. Their heads are close together, and they are talking low.

"Hey, Dad!" says Thalia Brown. She pulls at Dad's arm, but he keeps on talking to James.

"We're busy, Thalia," says James. "Go away."

Thalia sticks her tongue out at James.

"Thalia," says Dad, "James and I are talking now. Please stop pestering."

Thalia goes to Grandma. She leans against Grandma's arm as Grandma sings softly to the baby. He is almost asleep. Thalia touches his head. She likes the way his hair feels.

"Keep your hands to yourself, Thalia!" says Grandma.

Thalia goes outside. She sits on the cement of the small yard in back of her building, right under Miss Washington's laundry.

She runs her fingertips over the rough cement. It feels like sandpaper, like brick.

Near her foot Thalia sees something blue. She picks it up and rubs it against the cement. The chalk makes a powdery, uneven line. It does not go exactly where Thalia wants it to go—there are too many cracks in the cement.

Thalia stands up to look at her piece of blue. When she stands the cracks don't show so much. The shape looks like a blue bug—all it needs is legs. She draws legs and a house for the blue bug. Then she signs her name.

Thalia feels one drop of rain on her hand and another on her back. A raindrop falls on the blue bug. The light blue of the chalk turns wet, like blue mud.

The sky opens and all the water in the sky falls down. Thalia runs up the stairs to the back porch and stares out at the rain.

"Hey, rain!" she yells. "You leave my bug alone!"

The door on the second floor creaks open and Miss Washington runs down the stairs.

"My laundry!" she cries.

"My bug," says Thalia Brown.

Miss Washington and Thalia Brown stare at the rain and the laundry and the blue bug.

"Too bad," says Miss Washington.

"Too bad," says Thalia Brown.

The rain falls for hours.

When the rain stops, Grandma asks Thalia to go to the store for raisins. Thalia likes to go to the store. She skips almost all of the way there.

The grocery store is dark. Thalia finds the raisins and stands in line behind an old man with white hair. She looks at all the signs on the wall. One big sign with bright red letters catches Thalia's eye.

Thalia smiles widely. She can draw a picture and bring it to the Art Fair! She cannot wait to get home.

Back home, Thalia runs up the back porch steps and into the kitchen. The screen door slams behind her.

"Grandma!" cries Thalia Brown. "I'm going to be in an Art Fair! I need some paper, Grandma!"

"Hush!" says Grandma. "You'll wake the baby!" Grandma takes the raisins and change from Thalia's hands and walks away. Thalia waits until Grandma is gone. Then she creeps into James's bedroom.

James keeps some crayons in a shoebox under the bed. Thalia slides out the shoebox, and takes the whole box into the kitchen. Then she reaches up and grabs the shelf paper. Quickly she pulls the last piece of paper off the roll.

Thalia draws a blue bug with a blue crayon. She colors in the bug thick and smooth. She draws the bug's house and a blue leaf for the blue bug to eat. Then she signs her name.

James comes into the kitchen.

"What are you doing with my crayons!" he says. He snatches the box.

"I just used a blue one," says Thalia.

"You're always grabbing my stuff," says James. "You never ask me." He takes the crayons out of the kitchen.

"You never use them, James!" yells Thalia. She runs after him.

In the bedroom the baby starts to cry.

"Thalia Brown!" says Grandma. "You go quiet that baby down."

Thalia goes into the bedroom and hugs the baby over the crib rails.

"It's okay, Baby," says Thalia Brown. "James is just being mean. Go to sleep," she coos softly, rubbing circles on his back.

Baby closes his eyes. Thalia Brown tiptoes out of the bedroom. She goes back to the kitchen to look at her drawing. The paper is gone!

"Grandma," says Thalia, "have you seen my picture of the blue bug?"

"Oh," says Grandma. "You wanted to keep that? I thought it was trash." She pulls a crumpled paper from the garbage pail.

Thalia tries to smooth out the paper, but it will not stay flat. There is a grease spot right in the middle, on one of the blue bug's legs.

Thalia's eyes spill over. She runs out the back door and down the gray wooden stairs to the cement. She sits under Miss Washington's laundry. She stares at the blue smear that used to be the blue bug, and she cries as hard as the rain.

Miss Washington comes down the stairs to get her clothes off the line.

"Thalia Brown!" she says. "What are you doing under there crying like the rain?"

Thalia tells Miss Washington everything. She tells her about the blue bug, the Art Fair, and the picture Grandma threw in the garbage by mistake.

"Why, they're only a few setbacks," says Miss Washington. "You can't let a little disappointment stop you! Come upstairs with me. I

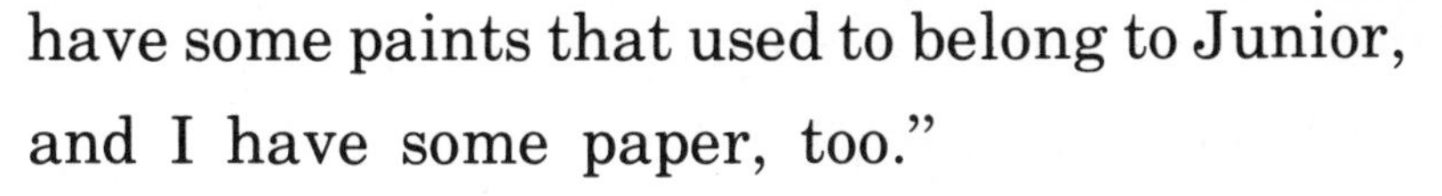

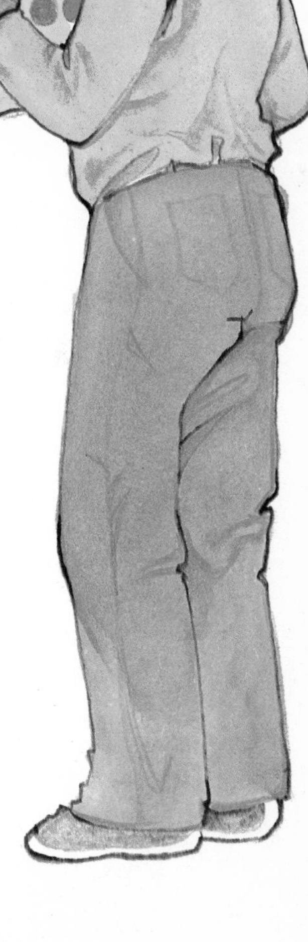

have some paints that used to belong to Junior, and I have some paper, too."

Thalia helps Miss Washington bring the clothes upstairs. Thalia puts the clothes-basket on the lace-covered kitchen table and looks around. Miss Washington goes into the front bedroom. In a minute she comes out with a paintbox and a whole pad of drawing paper.

"You can keep this paper—and the paints too."

Thalia has trouble thinking of a polite thing to say. Her mind is too busy seeing all the beautiful pictures she can make. She hugs the paintbox. "Thank you, Miss Washington," she says.

"You're welcome," says Miss Washington. "Show me what you've drawn when you're done."

Thalia takes the paintbox and the paper into a corner of the kitchen. Then she fills a bowl with water, sits down, and opens the paintbox. She dips the brush in the water and swishes it around the cake of blue paint. Then she begins to paint. She paints picture after picture.

Thalia Brown has been working so hard that only now she hears James's voice.

"Time for dinner, Thalia!" he says. "I've been calling you for an hour!"

"You have not," says Thalia. She keeps on painting.

"I have so," says James. He comes over to see what Thalia is doing. "Where'd you get the paints and paper?"

"Miss Washington. I'm going to be an artist when I grow up," she says.

"Yeah?" says James. "Come on. Let's eat."

After dinner Thalia shows her pictures to her dad. He looks at them all, slowly, one at a time.

"These are good, Thalia!" he says.

"She's going to be an artist when she grows up," says James.

Grandma listens while she feeds the baby.

"Did you say something about an art fair?" she asks.

"There's one Saturday at First Street Park," says Thalia.

Grandma nods. "Which picture are you going to enter?"

"I haven't made it yet," says Thalia.

Thalia sits at the kitchen table. As she opens her box of paints, James comes in, bringing his box of crayons.

"Do you want to use these?" he asks.

"Yes!" says Thalia. She takes the box and hugs it.

"You have to give them back!" says James. "They're still mine!"

"I will," says Thalia.

Thalia draws a blue bug with one of James's crayons and colors it in smooth and thick. Then she paints Thalia Brown drawing the blue bug. She paints in the cement and Miss Washington's laundry. When the paint is dry she takes a black crayon and prints her name, small and neat, in the bottom corner.

"That's not bad," says James. He leans over the back of Thalia's chair to look at her picture. "Not bad at all."

It seems as if Saturday morning will never come, but it does. It is hard for Thalia Brown to wait until after breakfast to take her picture to the Art Fair.

"I'm going to show my picture to Miss Washington," she tells Grandma Brown.

"You come right down here after that," says Grandma. "I'm going to the Art Fair with you."

"Good morning, Thalia Brown," says Miss Washington.

"Look, Miss Washington!" Thalia holds her picture up for Miss Washington to see.

"Well, that's fine!" says Miss Washington.

"Grandma's going to go with me to the Art Fair!" says Thalia.

"She sure must be proud of you!" says Miss Washington.

Thalia Brown skips along the sidewalk next to Grandma. Grandma pushes the stroller.

"Faster, Grandma!" says Thalia Brown.

"I'm going as fast as these old legs can," says Grandma. "You just worry about that picture, Thalia Brown! Don't you drop it."

The First Street Park looks very festive. A big sign in front says ART FAIR. Ribbons decorate the sign and nearby stands a wheelbarrow full of flowers. Inside more ribbons and flowers decorate two round tables. Some children's pictures are already hanging on the special display boards.

Thalia Brown shows her painting to a woman who is standing behind one of the round tables. The woman asks Thalia's name and age and what the title of the painting is.

Thalia Brown thinks.

"'Thalia Brown and the Blue Bug,'" she says.

The woman writes it down on a small piece of paper. She fixes Thalia's painting to a large sheet of bright construction paper to frame it, and glues the small paper with Thalia's name and age and "Thalia Brown and the Blue Bug" to a corner of the frame. Then she hangs Thalia's picture on a display board.

Thalia Brown is proud. So is Grandma. When another woman stops to look at Thalia's painting, Grandma Brown nods and says, "That's my granddaughter's picture. She's going to be an artist when she grows up."

"I'm an artist now," says Thalia Brown.

If I Were a Spider

If I were a spider,
on a summer morning,
I would string
the sparkling dew
in my web,
and catch the rising sun
for you.

—Kazue Mizumura

If I Were a Cricket

If I were a cricket,
all through the autumn nights
I would sing
for you,
a silver bell song
you would
never forget.

—*Kazue Mizumura*

The Seeing Stick

by Jane Yolen

Once in the ancient walled city of Peking there lived an emperor who had a daughter. Her name was Hwei Ming.

Now this daughter had ivory combs to smooth back her long black hair. She wore embroidered slippers on her feet, and her robes were woven of the finest silks. But rather than making her happy, such possessions made her

sad. For Hwei Ming was blind, and all the beautiful things in the kingdom brought her no pleasure at all.

Her father was also sad that his only daughter was blind, but he could not cry for her. He was the emperor, after all, and had given up weeping over such things when he took the throne.

Yet still he had hope that one day Hwei Ming might be able to see. So he decided that if someone could help her, such a person would be rewarded with a fortune in jewels. He sent word of his offer to all the towns and villages for hundreds of miles.

Monks came, of course, with their prayers and prayer wheels. They thought in this way to help Hwei Ming see. Magicians came, of course, with their charms and spells. They thought in this way to help Hwei Ming see. Doctors came, of course, with their potions and pins. They thought in this way to help Hwei Ming see.

But nothing could help. Hwei Ming had been blind from the day of her birth. No one could find a cure.

Now one day an old man, who lived far away, heard tales of the blind princess. He heard of the emperor's offer. And so he took his few possessions—a long walking stick, made from a single piece of golden wood, and his whittling knife—and started up the road. The sun rose hot on his right side and the sun set cool on his left as he traveled north to Peking to help the princess see.

At last the old man, his clothes tattered by his travels, stopped by the gate of the Outer City. The guards at the gate did not want to let such a ragged old man in.

"Grandfather, go home. There is nothing here for such as you," they said.

The old man touched their faces with his rough fingers. "So young," he said, "and already so old." He turned as if to go. Then he propped his walking stick against his side. He reached into his shirt for his whittling knife.

"What are you doing, grandfather?" said one of the guards when he saw the old man bring out the knife.

"I am going to show you my stick," said the old man, "for it is a stick that sees."

"Grandfather, that is nonsense," said the second guard.

"Just so, just so," said the old man. "But stranger things have happened." And so saying, he picked up the stick. He sharpened the knife three times.

As the guards watched, the old man told them how he had walked the many miles till he came to the walls of Peking. And as he told them his tale, he pointed to the pictures in the stick: an old man, his home, the long walk, the walls of Peking. And as they watched further, he began to cut their portraits into the wood.

The two guards looked at each other in amazement. They were flattered at their portraits on the old man's stick. Indeed, they had never seen such carving skill.

"Surely this is something the guards at the wall of the Inner City should see," they said. So, taking the old man by the arm, they guided him through the streets of the Outer City. They passed flower peddlers and rice sellers, silk weavers and jewel merchants, till they came to the great stone walls.

When the guards of the Inner City saw the seeing stick, they were surprised and delighted. "Carve our faces, too," they begged like children. And laughing, and touching their faces as any fond grandfather would, the old man did as they asked.

In no time at all, the guards of the Inner City took the old man by his arm and led him through the gate. They went to the great wooden doors of the palace.

Now when they arrived at the throne, it happened that Hwei Ming was sitting by the emperor's side. She was silent, sightless, and still. As the guards finished telling of the amazing pictures carved on the golden stick, the princess clapped her hands.

"Oh, I wish I could see that wonderful stick," she said.

"Just so, just so," said the old man. "And I will show it to you. For it is no ordinary piece of wood, but a stick that sees."

"What nonsense," said her father in a voice so low it was almost a growl.

But the princess did not hear him. She had already bent toward the sound of the old man's voice. "A seeing stick?"

The old man did not speak for a moment. Then he leaned forward and petted Hwei Ming's head and cheek. For though she was a princess, she was still a child. Then the old man began to tell again the story of his long journey to Peking. He carved each person and object—the old man, the guards, the great walls. And then he carved the wooden doors, the palace, and the princess.

When he finished, the old man reached out for the princess' small hands. He took her tiny fingers in his and placed them on the stick. Finger on finger, he helped her trace the pictures.

"Feel the long flowing hair of the princess," the old man said. "Like herself, it is straight and true." And Hwei Ming touched the carved stick. "Now feel your own long hair," he said. And she did.

"Feel the lines in the old man's face," he said, "from years of worry and years of joy." He placed the stick into her hands again. And the princess' slim fingers felt the carved stick. Then he put her fingers onto his face and traced the same lines there. It was the first time the princess had touched another person's face since she was a very small girl. The princess jumped up from her throne.

"Guards, O guards," she cried out. "Come here to me." And the guards lifted up their faces to the Princess Hwei Ming's hands. Her fingers, like little breezes, brushed their eyes and noses and mouths. Then she found each one on the carved stick.

Hwei Ming turned to her father, the emperor, who sat straight and tall on his great throne. She reached out and her fingers ran eagerly through his hair and down his nose and cheek. Then they rested on a tear they found there. And that was strange, indeed, for had not the emperor given up crying over such things when he took the throne?

They brought her through the streets of the city, then, the emperor in the lead. And Princess Hwei Ming touched men and women and children as they passed. At last she stood before the great walls of Peking and felt the stones themselves. Then she turned to the old man. Her voice was bright and full of laughter.

"Tell me another tale," she said.

"Tomorrow, if you wish," he replied.

For each tomorrow as long as he lived, the old man stayed with the royal family. The emperor rewarded him with a fortune in jewels, but the old man gave them all away.

Every day he told the princess a story. Some were tales as ancient as the city itself. Some were as new as the events of the day. And each time he carved wonderful images in the stick of golden wood.

As the princess listened, she grew eyes on the tips of her fingers. At least that is what she told the other blind children whom she taught to see as she saw. Certainly it was as true as saying she had a seeing stick. But the blind Princess Hwei Ming believed that both things were true.

And so did all the blind children in her city of Peking.

And so did the blind old man.

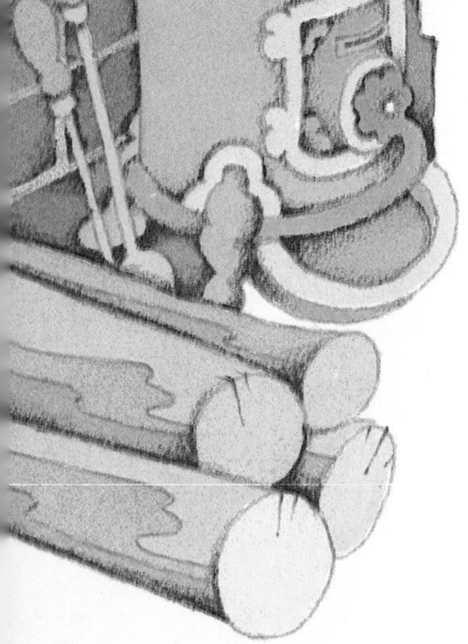

Pinocchio: The Tale of a Puppet

by Carlo Collodi

Master Cherry, the carpenter, finds a very unusual piece of wood.

There was once upon a time . . .

"A king!" all of my readers will instantly exclaim.

No, children, you are wrong. There was once upon a time a piece of wood.

This wood was not valuable. It was a log just like those that are burned in fireplaces to make a cheerful blaze and warm the rooms.

I cannot say how it came about, but the fact is, that one fine day this piece of wood was lying in the shop of an old carpenter by the name of Master Antonio. He was, however, called by everyone Master Cherry. This was because the end of his nose was as red and polished as a ripe cherry.

No sooner had Master Cherry set eyes on the piece of wood than his face beamed with delight. He thought of all the things he could make with the wood. His eyes sparkled as he rubbed his hands together with pleasure.

"This fine piece of wood has come at the right moment," he said to himself happily. "It will just do to make the leg of a little table."

Having said this, he immediately took a sharp axe with which to remove the bark and the rough surface. Just, however, as he was going to give the first stroke, he paused with his arm raised in the air. He heard a very small voice crying, "Do not strike me so hard!"

Picture to yourselves the astonishment of good old Master Cherry!

He turned his terrified eyes all around the room to try to discover where the little voice could possibly have come from, but he saw nobody! He looked under the bench—nobody. He looked into a cupboard that was always shut—nobody. He looked into a basket of shavings and sawdust—nobody. He even opened the door of the shop and gave a glance into the street—and still nobody. Who, then, could it be?

"I see how it is," he said, laughing and scratching his wig. "Evidently that little voice was all my imagination. Let us set to work again."

And taking up the axe he struck a tremendous blow on the piece of wood.

"Oh! Oh! You have hurt me!" cried the same little voice sorrowfully.

This time Master Cherry was petrified. His eyes started out of his head with fright, his mouth remained open, and his tongue hung out almost to the end of his chin, like a mask on a fountain. As soon as he had recovered the use of his speech, he began to stutter and tremble with fear.

"But where on earth can that little voice have come from?" he said. "Here there is certainly no living soul. Is it possible that this piece of wood could have learned to cry and to complain like a child? I cannot believe it. This piece of wood, here it is. It is a log for fuel like all the others, and thrown on the fire it would only be enough to boil a saucepan of beans. . . . How then? Can anyone be hidden inside it? I will find out at once!"

So saying, he took the piece of wood and started banging it against the floor and the walls of the room.

Then he stopped to listen for the sound of a little voice complaining. He waited two minutes—nothing; five minutes—nothing; ten minutes—still nothing!

"I see how it is," he then said, forcing himself to laugh and pushing up his wig. "Evidently the little voice that said 'Oh! Oh!' was all my imagination! Let us set to work again."

But since he was in a great fright, he tried to sing, to give himself courage.

Putting the axe aside he took his plane, to plane and polish the bit of wood. While he was running it up and down he heard someone laughing.

"Have done! You are tickling me all over!" said the voice.

This time poor Master Cherry fell down as if he had been struck by lightning. When he at last opened his eyes he found himself seated on the floor.

His face was quite changed. Even the end of his nose, instead of being bright red, as it was nearly always, had become blue from fright.

A Present for Geppetto

Master Cherry makes a present of the piece of wood to his friend Geppetto, who takes it to make a wonderful puppet, that will know how to dance, and to fence, and to leap like an acrobat.

At that moment someone knocked at the door.

"Come in," said the carpenter, without having the strength to rise to his feet.

A lively little old man immediately walked into the shop. His name was Geppetto. When the children in the neighborhood wished to make him angry they called him by the nickname of *Polendina*. This was because Geppetto's yellow wig greatly resembled polendina, a pudding made from corn.

Geppetto was very fiery. He became furious at anyone who called him Polendina, and there was no holding him.

"Good day, Master Antonio," said Geppetto. "What are you doing there on the floor?"

"I am teaching the alphabet to the ants."

"Much good that will do you."

"What has brought you to me, neighbor Geppetto?"

"My legs. But to tell the truth, Master Antonio, I have come to ask a favor."

"Here I am, ready to serve you," replied the carpenter, getting on his knees.

"This morning an idea came into my head."

"Let us hear it."

"I thought I would make a beautiful wooden puppet, a wonderful puppet that should know how to dance, to fence, and to leap like an acrobat. With this puppet I would travel about the world to earn food and drink. What do you think of it?"

"Bravo, Polendina!" exclaimed the same little voice, and it was impossible to say where it came from.

Hearing himself called Polendina, Geppetto became very red in the face from rage. He turned to the carpenter and gave him an angry look.

"Why do you insult me?" he said.

"Who insults you?"

"You called me Polendina! . . ."

"It was not I!"

"Would you have it, then, that it was I? It was you, I say!"

"No!"

"Yes!"

"No!"

"Yes!"

And becoming more and more angry, from words they came to blows. The two friends flew at each other and fought and fought. They could not hear the sound of someone laughing softly.

When the fight was over Master Antonio was in possession of Geppetto's yellow wig, and Geppetto discovered that the gray wig belonging to the carpenter had remained between his teeth.

"Give me back my wig," screamed Master Antonio.

"And you, return me mine, and let us make friends."

The two men, having recovered their wigs, shook hands and swore they would remain friends to the end of their lives.

"Well, then, neighbor Geppetto," said the carpenter, to prove that peace was made, "what is the favor that you wish of me?"

"I want a little wood to make my puppet. Will you give me some?"

Master Antonio was delighted, and he immediately went to the bench and picked up the piece of wood that had caused him so much fear. But just as he was going to give it to his friend the piece of wood gave a shake. It wriggled out of his hands and struck with all of its force against Geppetto's knees.

"Ah! Is that the courteous way in which you give your presents, Master Antonio? You have almost broken my knees!"

"I swear to you that it was not I! . . ."

"Then you would have it that it was I? . . ."

"The wood is entirely to blame! . . ."

"I know that it was the wood; but it was you that hit my legs with it! . . ."

"I did not hit you with it! . . ."

"You foolish man! Of course you did!"

"Geppetto, don't insult me or I will call you Polendina!"

"Mule!"

"Polendina!"

"Donkey!"

"Polendina!"

"Baboon!"

"Polendina!"

On hearing himself called Polendina for the third time, Geppetto was furious. He fell upon the carpenter and they fought once again. Neither of them could hear a soft, little laugh.

When the battle was over, Master Antonio had two more scratches on his nose, and Geppetto had two buttons too few on his waistcoat. Their quarrel being thus settled, they shook hands and swore to remain good friends for the rest of their lives.

Geppetto carried off his fine piece of wood and, thanking Master Antonio, returned limping to his house.

A Puppet Is Made

Geppetto begins at once to make a puppet, which he names Pinocchio. He soon finds out that it is an unusual puppet.

Geppetto lived in a small ground-floor room. The only light was in the staircase. Geppetto's furniture could not have been simpler—a bad chair, a poor bed, and a broken-down table. At the end of the room there was a fireplace with a lighted fire; but the fire was painted. By the fire was a painted saucepan that was boiling cheerfully. It sent out a cloud of smoke that looked exactly like real smoke.

Geppetto took his tools and set to work. He began to cut out the puppet, which would one day earn him food and drink.

"What name shall I give him?" he said to himself. "I think I will call him Pinocchio. It is a name that will bring him luck. I once knew a whole family so called. There was Pinocchio the father, Pinocchia the mother, and Pinocchi the children, and all of them did well. The richest of them was a beggar."

Having found a name for his puppet, he began to work in good earnest, and he first made his hair, then his forehead, and then his eyes.

The eyes being finished, imagine his astonishment when he noticed that they moved and looked fixedly at him.

Geppetto, seeing himself stared at by those two wooden eyes, almost dropped the puppet.

"Wicked wooden eyes, why do you look at me?" he said.

No one answered.

He then proceeded to carve the nose; but no sooner had he made it than it began to grow. And it grew, and grew, and grew, until in a few minutes it had become an immense nose that seemed as if it would never end.

Poor Geppetto tired himself out with cutting it off. The more he cut and shortened it, the longer did that bold nose become!

The mouth was not even completed when it began to laugh and make fun of him.

"Stop laughing!" said Geppetto, annoyed, but he might as well have spoken to the wall.

"Stop laughing, I say!" he roared in a threatening tone.

The mouth then ceased laughing, but put out its tongue.

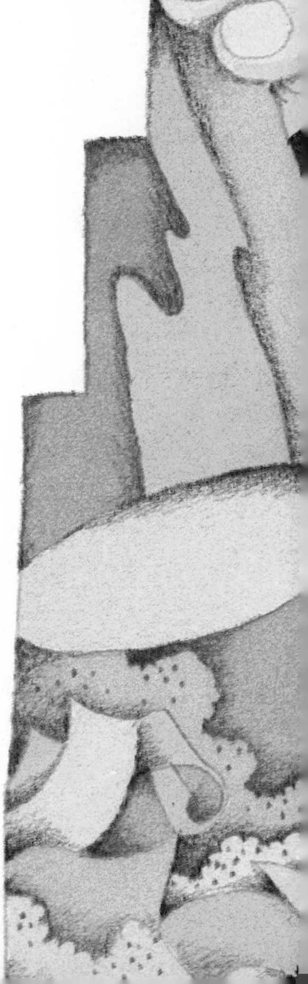

Geppetto, not to spoil his handiwork, pretended not to see, and continued his labors. After the mouth he shaped the chin, then the throat, then the shoulders, the stomach, the arms and the hands.

The hands were scarcely finished when Geppetto felt his wig snatched from his head. He turned around, and what did he see? He saw his yellow wig in the puppet's hand.

"Pinocchio! . . . Give me back my wig instantly!"

But Pinocchio, instead of returning it, put it on his own head, and was as a result nearly smothered.

Geppetto, at this rude and scornful behavior, felt sadder than he had ever been in his life before. He turned to Pinocchio and began to shout at him.

"You young rascal! You are not yet completed, and you are already beginning to show want of respect to your father! That is bad, my boy, very bad!"

And he dried a tear.

The legs and the feet remained to be done.

When Geppetto had finished the feet he received a kick on the point of his nose.

"I deserve it!" he said to himself. "I should have thought of it sooner! Now it is too late!"

He then took the puppet under the arms and placed him on the floor to teach him to walk.

Pinocchio's legs were stiff and he could not move, but Geppetto led him by the hand and showed him how to put one foot before the other.

When his legs became flexible, Pinocchio began to walk by himself and to run about the room, until, having gone out of the house door, he jumped into the street and escaped.

Poor Geppetto rushed after him but was not able to overtake him. That rascal Pinocchio leaped in front of him like a hare. The puppet knocked his wooden feet together against the pavement, making as much clatter as twenty pairs of peasants' clogs.

"Stop him! Stop him!" shouted Geppetto. But the people in the street, seeing a puppet running like a racehorse, stood still in amazement to look at it. They laughed, and laughed, and laughed.

At last, as good luck would have it, a soldier arrived who, hearing the uproar, imagined that a colt had escaped from his master. Planting himself courageously with his legs apart in the middle of the road, he waited with the determined purpose of stopping him, and thus preventing the chance of worse disasters.

When Pinocchio, still at some distance, saw the soldier blocking the whole street, he tried to take him by surprise and to pass between his legs. But he failed completely.

The soldier, without disturbing himself in the least, caught him cleverly by the nose. It was an immense nose that seemed made on purpose to be laid hold of by soldiers. He turned him over to Geppetto. Wishing to punish him, Geppetto intended to pull his ears at once. But imagine his feelings when he could not succeed in finding them. And do you know the reason? It was that, in his hurry to model him, he had forgotten to make them.

He then took him by the collar. As he was leading him away he scolded him, shaking his head threateningly.

"We will go home at once. And as soon as we arrive I will take care of you, never doubt it."

At this announcement Pinocchio threw himself on the ground and would not take another step. In the meanwhile a crowd of curious people began to gather and to make a ring around them.

Some of them said one thing, some another.

"Poor puppet!" said several. "He is right not to wish to return home! Who knows how Geppetto will beat him! . . ."

And some others added harshly, "Geppetto seems a good man but with boys he is a cruel master! If that poor puppet is left in his hands he is quite capable of tearing him in pieces! . . ."

It ended in so much being said and done that the soldier at last set Pinocchio free and sent Geppetto to prison for a few days.

As Geppetto was being led away to prison, he sobbed out: "Wretched boy! And to think how I have tried to make him a well-mannered puppet!"

After quite a long time, and many unusual adventures, Pinocchio finally returned to Geppetto.

Dancer

by Byrd Baylor

Sometimes I dance mountains,
and whirlwinds,
and water,
and bubbles.

And I even
dance bugs—
crawly bugs,
bugs with wings,
purple bugs that shine.

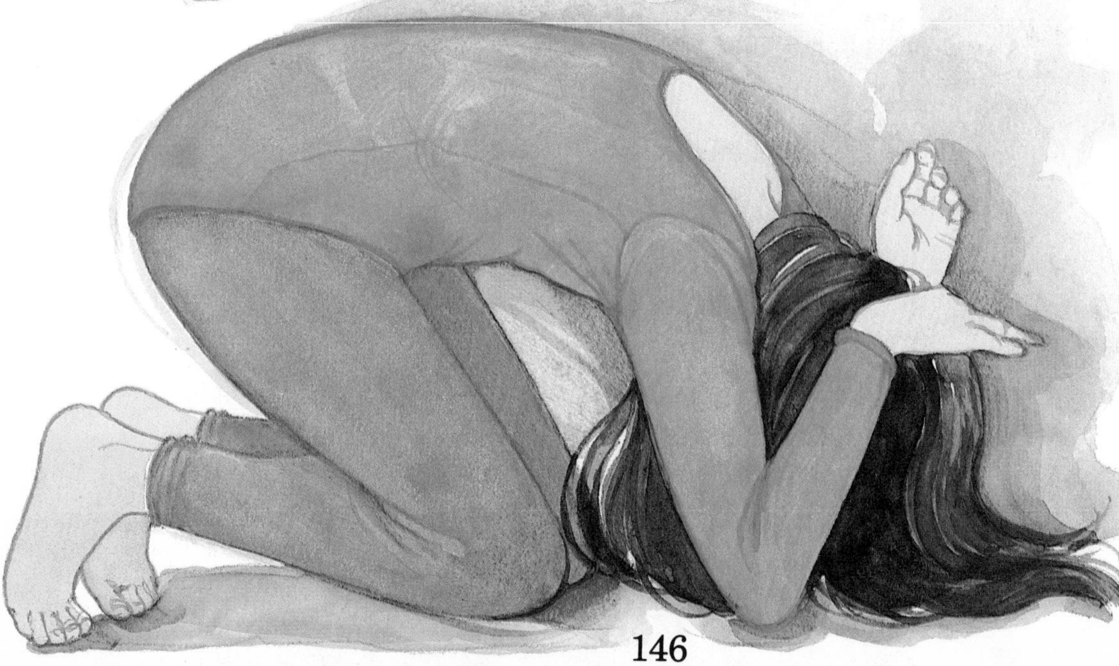

Sometimes
I let
my hands
have a dance
of their own,
and sometimes
my feet,
and even
my nose
wants to
wiggle itself
in a nose dance.
(I let it.)

Now
it's a
slow
slow
dance that I do,
a dance
I made out of
all the slowest
slow things
in the world—

like
small blades of grass
growing
and a sleepy
fat earthworm
turning
around
in the damp, dark earth. . . .

Then
I
EXPLODE
into
a thousand lightning flashes
and a million falling stars
and fire fire FIRE!
Whatever's
fast.

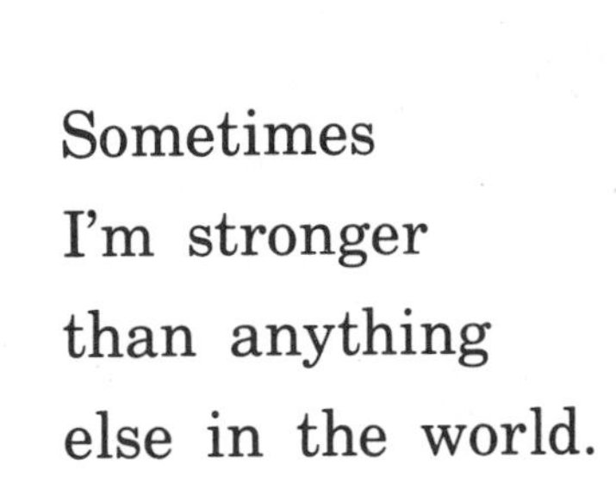

Sometimes
I'm stronger
than anything
else in the world.

Then I dance
a mountain
and that mountain
reaches
from here
to the sky.

Sometimes
I dance
all things
that are OPEN—

the wide wide sky
or
a flower with
full floppy petals
(probably orange).

And then
I dance
the feeling
of things that are
CLOSED—

like a seed pod
holding
its seeds.

OPEN
CLOSE.

OPEN
CLOSE.

Dancing
is a way
of talking
because
a dance
can say
anything.

It can say
I'm happy
or
I'm sad
or
I'm ALIVE
and
I feel like
moving in
my own special
dance.

I dance my way.
Now it's your turn.
What's *your* way?

The Acrobats

I'll swing
By my ankles,
She'll cling
To your knees
As you hang
By your nose
From a high-up
Trapeze.
But just one thing, please,
As we float through the breeze—
Don't sneeze.

—Shel Silverstein

UNIT FOUR

Do You Believe in Magic?

Brownie in the Farmyard

by Dinah Marie Mulock

There was once a little Brownie who lived in a coal cellar. A Brownie is a strange creature. He is a little old man, about a foot high. He is all dressed in brown, with a brown face, brown hands, and a brown cap, just the color of a brown mouse. And, like a mouse, he hides in corners and only comes out when no one is around.

If you were to go into the English countryside, you would hear many funny stories about Brownies. So I may as well tell you the adventures of one particular Brownie, who belonged to a family there.

In this family, there were six children, a mother, and a father, who was a Gardener. All the children declared that a Brownie often came to play with them.

Brownie was supposed to live in the cellar, under a lump of coal. Ever since the family could remember, there had always been a bowl of milk put behind the coal cellar door for the Brownie's supper. Perhaps he drank it. Perhaps he did not. Anyhow, the bowl was always empty the next morning.

One day Brownie overheard the Gardener and his wife having a silly quarrel.

"You make such a fuss over your pigs, and get all the scraps for them," said the wife. "It's of much more importance that I should have all the scraps for my lovely ducklings."

"*Lovely* ducklings? Impossible!"

"They *are* lovely and you know it!"

"Why would you raise ducklings at all? Fine fat chickens would be better. You'll find out your mistake some day."

"And so will you when your prize cow runs out of milk. You'll wish you had taken my advice and sold her."

The next morning the couple rose early, as usual, to begin their chores. The wife went out to feed the fowl and collect the eggs. Her husband began the gardening work before breakfast. But Brownie had done his mischief long before dawn.

When all the fowls came running to be fed, the big hen who had hatched the ducklings was seen wandering sadly about and clucking for her young brood. She could not find them anywhere. If she had been able to speak, she might have told how a large white duck had waddled into the farmyard and waddled out again, coaxing them after her, no doubt in search of a pond. But whether she could speak or not, they were missing, most certainly.

"Cluck, cluck, cluck!" mourned the miserable mother hen.

"Oh, my ducklings, my ducklings!" cried the Gardener's wife. "Who could have carried off my beautiful ducklings?"

"Rats, maybe," said the Gardener, cruelly, as he walked away. And as he went he heard the squeak of a rat below his wheelbarrow. But he could not catch it, any more than his wife could catch the large white duck. Of course not. Both were—the Brownie!

Just at this moment the six children of the family came running into the farmyard. When

they had been especially good, they were sometimes allowed to go milking with their father, the Gardener, each carrying a mug for a drink of milk. They scampered after him, a noisy group, begging to be taken down to the field, and holding out their six mugs.

"What, six mugs of milk, when I haven't any to spare, and your mother is always wanting more? You may come to the field, but you'll get no milk this day. Take your mugs back to the kitchen."

Although disappointed, the children obeyed. Then they followed the Gardener to the field.

Brownie Magic

It was such a beautiful morning that the children were soon happy again. They merrily skipped across the field. The grass shone with dew, like a sheet of diamonds, the clover smelled sweet, and two skylarks were singing to one another high up in the sky. Several rabbits darted past, to the children's great joy. One very large rabbit, brown, not gray, dodged in and out among them, and once nearly tripped the Gardener, pail and all, by running across his feet. This set them all laughing until they came to where Dolly, the cow, lay chewing her cud under a large oak tree.

It was great fun to stir her up, as usual, and lie down, one after the other, in the place where she had lain all night long making the grass flat, and warm and perfumy with her sweet breath. She let them do it, and then stood meekly by, for Dolly was the gentlest cow in the world.

But this morning something strange seemed to be the matter with her. She altogether refused to be milked. She kicked, lunged, and knocked over the pail, which was empty.

"Bless the cow! What's wrong with her? It's surely you children's fault. Stand off, all of you. Soh, Dolly! Good Dolly!"

But Dolly was anything but good. She stood switching her tail and looking as savage as so mild an animal possibly could look.

"It's all your doing, you naughty children! You've been playing some trick on her, I know," cried the Gardener in great anger.

They told him they had done nothing, and indeed they looked as quiet as mice and as innocent as lambs. Finally, the biggest boy pointed out a large wasp which had settled in Dolly's ear.

"That accounts for everything," said the Gardener.

But it did not solve everything. When he tried to drive it away it kept coming back again and again, buzzing around his own head as well as the cow's. Its voice, the children thought, was less like the buzz of a wasp than the sound of a person laughing. At last it frightened Dolly so much that with one wild bound she darted away and ran off to the far end of the field.

"I'll get a rope and tie her legs together," cried the Gardener fiercely. "She shall be sorry for giving me all this trouble—that she shall!"

"Ha, ha, ha!" laughed somebody. The Gardener thought it was the children. He gave one of them an angry look as he walked away to the house. But they knew it was somebody else. They were not at all surprised when, the minute his back was turned, Dolly came walking quietly back. She was led by a little brown man who scarcely reached up to her knees. Yet she let him guide her, which he did as gently as possible, though the string he held her by was no thicker than a spider web floating from one of her horns.

"Soh, Dolly! Good Dolly!" cried Brownie, mimicking the Gardener's voice. "Now we'll

see what we can do. I want my breakfast badly, don't you, little ones?"

Of course they did, for the morning air made them very hungry.

"Very well, wait a bit, though. Old people should be served first, you know. Besides, I want to go to bed," said the Brownie.

Go to bed in the daylight! The children all laughed, and then looked quite shy and sorry, since they might have seemed rude to the Brownie. But he liked fun and never minded a friendly joke.

He placed himself on the milking stool, which was so high that his little legs were dangling halfway down, and milked and milked. Dolly stood as still as possible until he had filled the whole pail. She gave as much milk as two cows. And such delicious milk it was, all frothing and yellow, richer than Dolly's milk had ever been before.

All the children's mouths watered, but not a word did they say. Instead of giving it to them, Brownie put his own mouth to the pail and drank and drank, until it seemed as if he were never going to stop. But it was certainly a

relief to them when he popped his head up again. The pail was as full as ever! The children's eyes were wide with excitement.

The Brownie winked at them and smiled. "Now, little ones, it's your turn. Where are your mugs?" he asked.

All answered mournfully, "We have none. Father made us take them back to the kitchen again."

"Never mind. Gather me half-a-dozen of the biggest buttercups you can find."

"What nonsense!" thought the children; but they did it. Brownie laid the flowers in a row upon the oldest girl's lap. He blew upon them one by one, and each turned into the most beautiful golden cup that ever was seen!

"Now, then, everyone take a mug, and I'll fill it."

He milked away. Each child had a drink, and then the cups were filled again. And all the while Dolly stood as quietly as possible, happy to supply milk to the whole village, if the Brownie desired it.

"Soh, Dolly! Thank you, Dolly!" said he again, mimicking the Gardener's voice, half growling, half coaxing. And while he spoke, the real voice of the Gardener was heard behind the hedge. There was a sound like a great wasp flying away, which made Dolly prick up her ears. The children snatched up their mugs, but there was no need. They had all turned into buttercups again.

The Gardener jumped over the fence as cross as two sticks, with an old rope in his hand.

"Oh, what a bother I've had! Breakfast ready, and no milk yet. Such a fuss they are making over those lost ducklings. Stand back you children, and don't bother me a bit. No use begging, not a drop of milk shall you get. Hello, Dolly! Quiet, old girl!"

Dolly was quiet enough this time, but you might as well have milked a plaster cow in a toy store. Not one ringing drop tinkled against the empty pail. When the children peeped in, they saw, to their surprise, that it was empty.

"The creature's under a spell!" cried the Gardener in a great fury. "Or else somebody has milked her dry already. Have you done it? Or you?" he asked each child.

They might have said No, which was the actual truth, but then it would not have been the whole truth. They knew quite well that Dolly had been milked, and also who had done it. Their mother had always taught them that to make a person believe a lie is nearly as bad as telling the lie. Yet still they did not like to betray the kind little Brownie. Greatly puzzled, they hung their heads and said nothing.

"Look in your pail again," cried a voice from the other side of Dolly. And there at the bottom was just the usual amount of milk—no more and no less.

The Gardener was very much astonished. "It must be the Brownie!" muttered he in a frightened tone. Then, taking off his hat, "Thank

you, sir," said he to the Brownie, at which the children all burst out laughing. But they said nothing, and he was afraid to ask them any more questions.

By and by, his fright wore off a little. "I only hope the milk is good and will not poison anybody," said he in a bad mood. "However, that's not my affair. You children had better tell your mother all about it. I left her in the farmyard in a sad state of mind about her ducklings."

Perhaps Brownie heard this, and was sorry, for he liked the children's mother, who had always been kind to him. Besides, he never did harm to anybody who did not deserve it. Being a Brownie, he could hardly be said to have a conscience, but he did like to see people happy rather than miserable.

Mother Hen

Brownie did not go to bed under his big lump of coal for the day. After breakfast, when the children and their mother came out to look for the ducklings again, he crept after them, and hid behind the hen coop. The mother hen was there, but the young ones were nowhere to be seen.

The children could remember how happy the hen had been with the ducklings. There had been eight in the brood, and how funny they were! They looked so innocent, yet wise, as ducklings do. When the hen clucked, they quacked in answer. They enjoyed peering out at the world from under the hen's wing, or hopping over her back, or snuggling all together by her side. Then nothing could be seen of them except a mass of yellow legs. They looked like a giant centipede. But now the hen was alone, and the ducklings could not be found.

"How sad the old hen is," said the oldest child, looking at the lonesome hen with pity. The hen had hatched the ducklings and kept wandering about the farmyard, clucking miserably.

"Those poor ducklings," said the children's mother. "What could have become of them? If rats had killed them, we would have found feathers or something. They must have been stolen, or wandered away and died of cold and hunger."

The children's mother sighed, for she could not bear any living thing to suffer. The children nearly cried at the thought of what might be happening to their pretty ducklings. That very minute, a wee brown face peered through a hole in the hen coop, making the old mother

hen fly furiously at it. This she did at the slightest hint of an enemy coming near her little ones.

However, no harm happened. A guinea fowl suddenly ran across the farmyard, screaming in its usual harsh voice. It was not the usual sort of guinea fowl, but one larger and handsomer than any of theirs.

"Oh, what a beautiful creature! How did it ever come into our farmyard?" cried the delighted children. They started off after it, to catch it if possible.

But they ran and they ran, through the gate and out into the lane. The guinea fowl still ran on before them, turning around a corner. The children lost sight of it, but they saw something else, equally strange.

Sitting on the top of a big thistle, so big that he must have had to climb it just like a tree, was the Brownie. His legs were crossed and his arms too. His little brown cap was stuck boldly on one side, and he was laughing heartily.

"How do you do? Here I am again. I thought I wouldn't go to bed after all. Shall I help you find the ducklings? Very well! Come along."

They crossed the field, Brownie running beside them as fast as they could run, though he looked like such an old man. Sometimes he turned over on his legs and arms doing a cartwheel. They tried to imitate him, but generally failed.

He led them on and on until they came to the wood, and to a green path in it, which, well as they knew the neighborhood, none of the children had ever seen before. It led to a most beautiful pond, as clear as crystal and as blue as the sky. Large trees grew around it, dipping their branches in the water, as if they were looking at themselves in a glass. All about their roots were primroses, the biggest primroses the children had ever seen.

Down they dropped on their fat knees, squashing down more primroses than they gathered, though they tried to gather them all. The smallest child even began to cry because her hands were so full that the flowers dropped through her fingers.

But the older children had no time for the primroses. "I thought we had come to look for ducklings," said the oldest. "Mother is fretting dreadfully about her ducklings. Where can they be?"

"Shut your eyes and you'll see," said the Brownie. They all laughed, but shut their eyes. When they opened their eyes again, what should they see but a whole fleet of ducklings, sailing out from the roots of an old willow tree, one after the other. They were swimming as naturally as if they had lived on a pond, and this particular pond, all their lives.

"Count them," said the Brownie, "the whole eight, quite correct. Try to catch them, if you can."

This was easier said than done. The children set to work with pleasure. Children enjoy chasing something. They coaxed them. They shouted at them. They threw little sticks at them. But, as soon as they wanted them to go one way, the fleet of ducklings immediately turned around and sailed another way. They did it so seriously and grandly that the children could not help laughing.

As for little Brownie, he sat on a branch of the willow tree, with his legs dangling down to the surface of the pond, kicking at the water spiders and grinning with all his might. At length, quite tired out in spite of their fun, the children begged for his help, and he took pity on them.

"Turn around three times and see what you can find," shouted the Brownie.

Immediately each boy found in his arms, and each little girl in her apron, a fine fat duck-

ling. Because there were eight of them, the two older children had two each. They were rather cold and damp, and slightly uncomfortable to cuddle. Poor things! They struggled hard to get away. But the children hugged them tight and ran as fast as their legs could carry them through the wood, forgetting in their joy even to say "Thank you" to the little Brownie.

When they reached their mother she was as glad as they. She never expected to see her ducklings again. To have them all back alive and well, and to watch them running to the old hen, who welcomed them with delight, was so exciting that nobody thought of asking a single question about how they had been found.

When the mother did ask, the children told her all about Brownie's taking them to the beautiful pond. "And what a wonderful pond it was," they said. They told her how green the trees were around it, and how large the primroses grew. They never tired of talking about it, and looking for it. But the odd thing was, that look as they might, they never could find it again. Many a day the little ones roamed about, one by one or all together, around the woods, and across the woods, and up and down the woods. They often got themselves sadly bedraggled with mud, and torn with brambles; but they never found the beautiful pond again.

Nor did the ducklings, for they wandered no more from the farmyard, to the old mother hen's great satisfaction. They grew up into fat ducks—five white ones and three gray ones, and waddled about, very happy.

Dawn Saunders, Magician

An Interview

Dawn, how did you become interested in magic?

Well, my father and my brother are magicians. And my father owns a magic shop. Most Saturdays I go to the shop with my dad. I practice my magic and act as my dad's assistant when he does tricks for the customers.

Sometimes I help with the customers. If I know how to do a certain trick, I'll do the trick for the customer.

How long have you been doing magic tricks?

I started about five years ago, when I was five years old.

Do you do tricks only for your family and friends or do you ever put on shows for special groups?

When I was six, I did some magic tricks on a local TV program. I was on the show two or three times.

I've done two shows for the Cub Scouts, one at Halloween and one a few weeks ago. I also performed in a talent show at school. They announced the winners' names over the loud-speaker. I listened for "Dawn Saunders"—then I heard it!

I was on the TV news once, too. At a magic convention, I went over to a magician's booth. I said, "Hey, Bob, look what I just learned!" I showed him a card trick, and the people on the news team filmed me.

Could you do one of your card tricks for us?

Sure. This one is called "Coin Assembly." I have four quarters and four kings. I place a king on top of each quarter.

The first king got greedy. He wanted the second king's quarter. So he took it, as you can see.

But he still felt greedy. He took the third king's quarter, too.

He got greedier and greedier. And, as you might be able to guess, he also took the fourth king's quarter.

That was great! Could you do it again, s-l-o-w-l-y?

Sorry! I can only do a trick once a day.

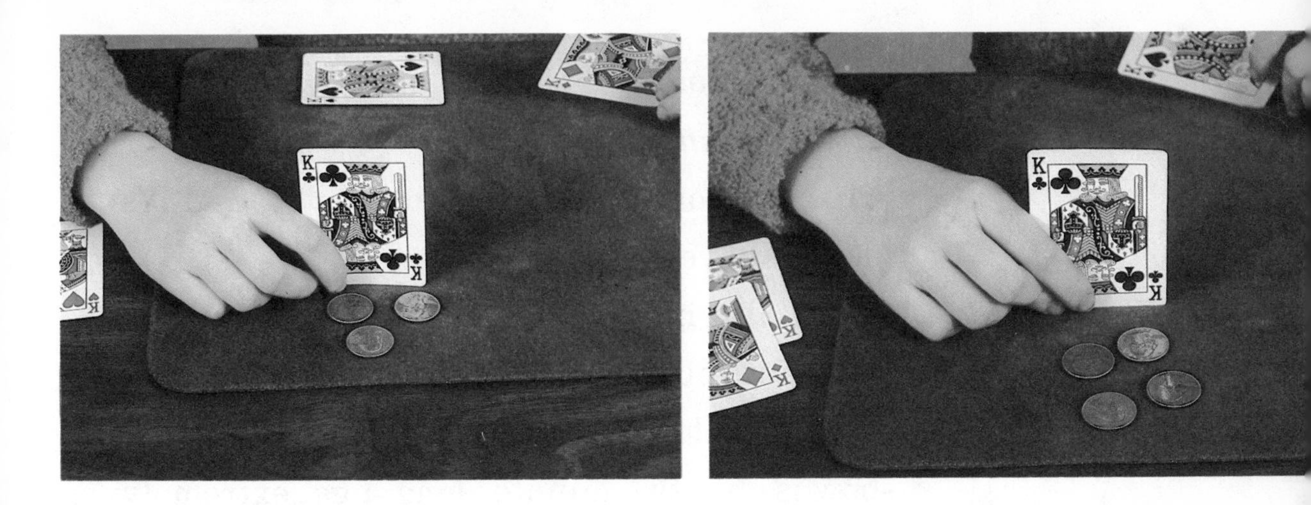

Do you ever teach magic to others?

Lots of magicians come in here and teach *me!* My father has a school and he teaches magic, mostly to teenagers.

I belong to a magicians' club. We watch each other do magic, and I learn a lot of tricks.

Sometimes my friends ask, "How did you do that trick?" Once in a while I'll show them, but not very often.

Have you ever made a mistake on stage?

Yes. I don't like to mention that! I was doing a trick in which you turn a bag into a silk scarf. Well, I made a mistake, but I was able to cover it up. The audience didn't catch on—they still clapped.

To be a good magician, what talents do you think you should have?

I think you should be a good actor, and it's nice to have a sense of humor.

You also have to *try* not to be nervous. It's hard, but you've got to try. I usually drink a lot of water before and after a show. Even if the show is only two minutes long, I get extremely thirsty. I have no idea why, but many magicians do.

Are there any magicians whom you admire?

Oh, lots! Do I have to name them all? Jimmy Ray is a great magician and we're friends. I'm also fond of Doug Henning, David Copperfield, and many others.

Is magic an expensive hobby?

(smiling) Well, not for me. I'm lucky because my dad has a magic shop. I get all my stuff for free.

But some of the easier tricks cost about one or two dollars.

Do you hope to have a career as a magician someday?

I have my fantasies about magic. I'm still thinking, of course, but I might like to be a psychologist or a magician—someone who cheers people up. And I think a magician is very good at that.

Do you have any advice for kids who might want to be magicians?

I would tell them to go into a local magic shop. They should tell the sales clerk that they want to start doing magic tricks. The clerk will help them get started. They could also go to the library and take out a book on magic.

Dawn, could you do another trick for us?

Sure, but I'll need to borrow two rings. This trick is called "Blackbeard's Chest." I have two shoelaces, a toy harpoon, two rings, and a small chest.

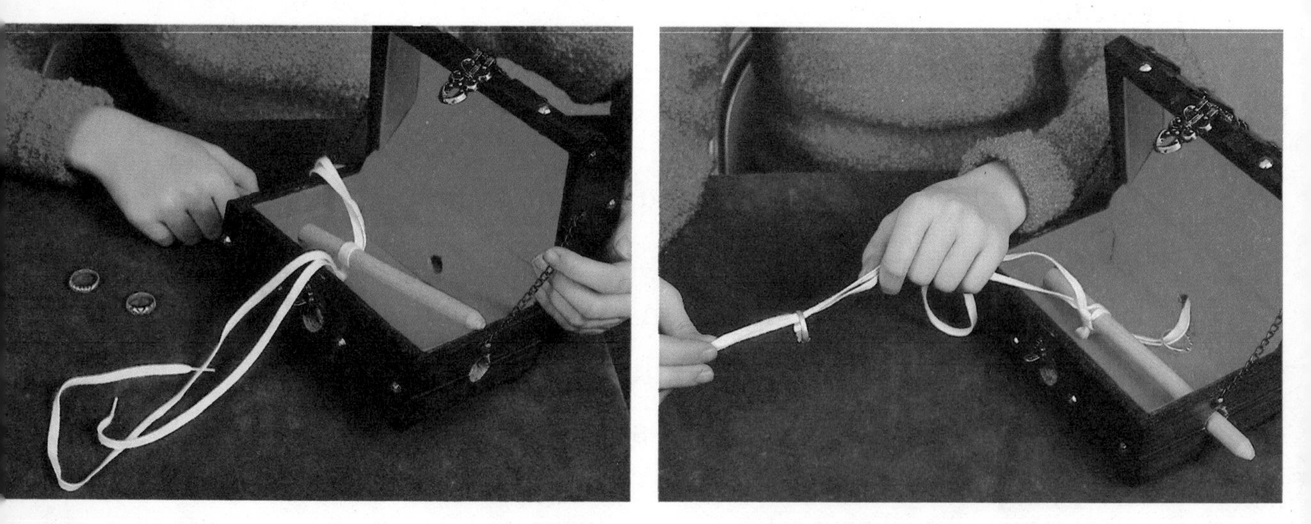

I tie the shoelaces to the harpoon and put the harpoon through the holes in the chest. I use the shoelaces to tie the rings to the harpoon. Then I tie the laces on top of the chest.

The rings are tied up pretty well, aren't they? But this happens to be a magic harpoon. I push it right through the holes, and the rings fall off the shoelaces.

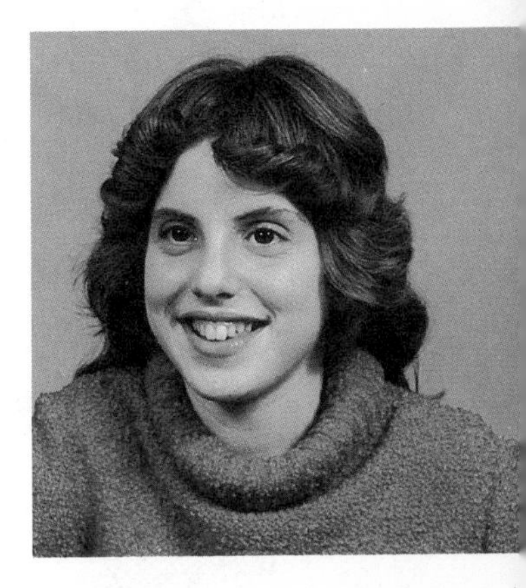

It looks like magic. But tell us, Dawn, how did they really come off?

(smiling and giving back rings) Very well, I thought!

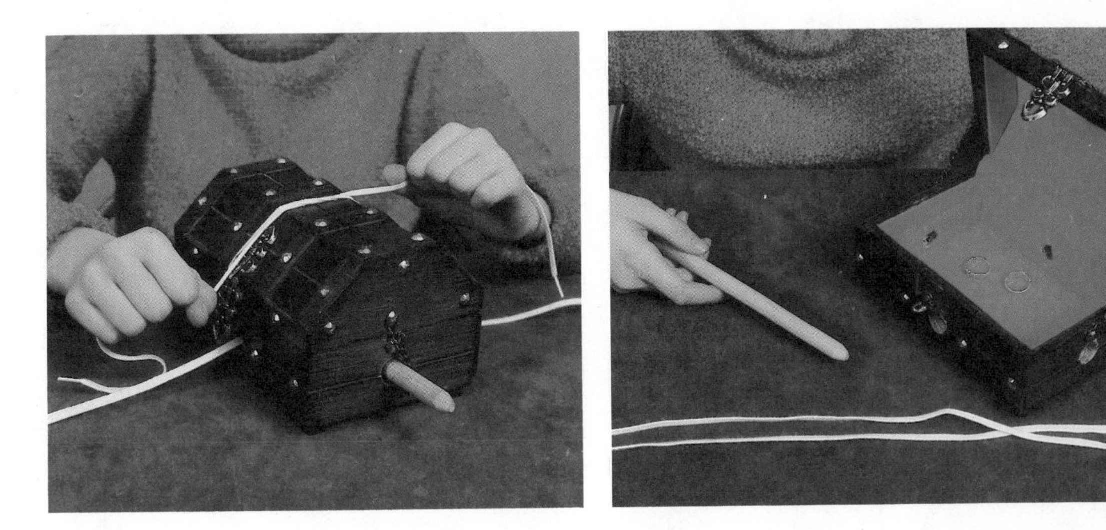

Magic Tricks

The Magic Balloon

by Rose Wyler and Gerald Ames

The Trick: Drop an empty balloon into a bag and blow. Then pull out a blown-up balloon!

The Secret: A second, blown-up balloon is inside the bag. That is the one you pull out.

Materials:

2 blown-up balloons (same color, size)

1 large paper bag

transparent tape

1. Before the show, tape a balloon to the inside of the bag. Drop the other balloon in on top.

2. Reach into the bag and pull out the top balloon. Let the air out and drop the balloon into the bag. Bend over the bag and blow, blow, blow.

3. Pull out the blown-up balloon.

The Mystery Marble

by Rose Wyler and Gerald Ames

The Trick: Cover a marble with a cloth. Remove the cloth and the marble is gone!

The Secret: Your helper takes the marble.

Materials:

marble, cloth

1. Show a marble in your hand. Cover your hand with a cloth.

2. Say, "Feel under the cloth. Is the marble still there?" The last one to check is your helper, who takes the marble away. When you remove the cloth, the marble is gone.

3. Cover your hand again and say, "Is the marble still missing?" After everyone checks, remove the cloth. Your helper has put the marble back.

The Broken Toothpick

by Barbara Seuling

The Trick: A toothpick, wrapped up in a handkerchief, is broken in two. Shake out the handkerchief, and the toothpick falls out unbroken.

The Secret: A second toothpick, hidden in the hem of the handkerchief, is the one that is broken. The one wrapped up is not harmed.

Materials:

2 toothpicks, 1 handkerchief

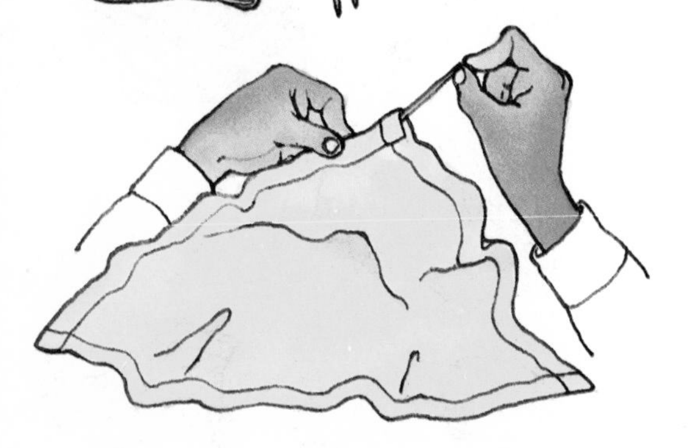

1. Before the show, slide one toothpick into the hem of the handkerchief, near a corner.

2. Lay the handkerchief out flat, holding the corner with the toothpick with your fingers.

3. Show the other toothpick to the audience. Place it on the handkerchief.

4. Fold the handkerchief. Let the loose toothpick fall to the left and bottom. Move the hidden toothpick toward the top.

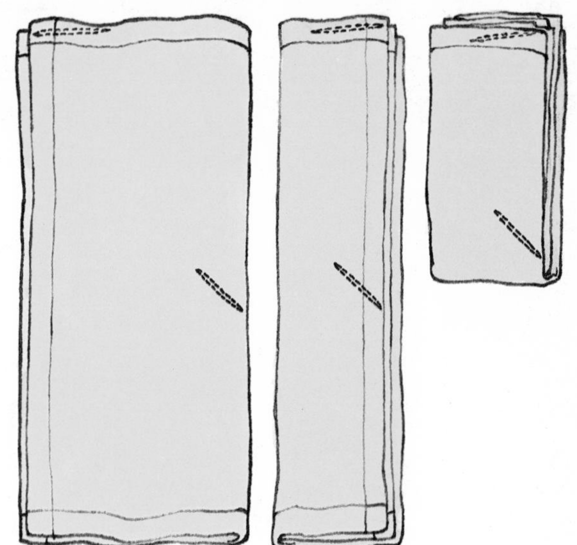

5. As you feel the toothpick beneath the folds, ask someone from the audience to break the toothpick in two. (Be sure you hold up the secret one to break.) You will hear the snap. The audience will agree that the toothpick is broken.

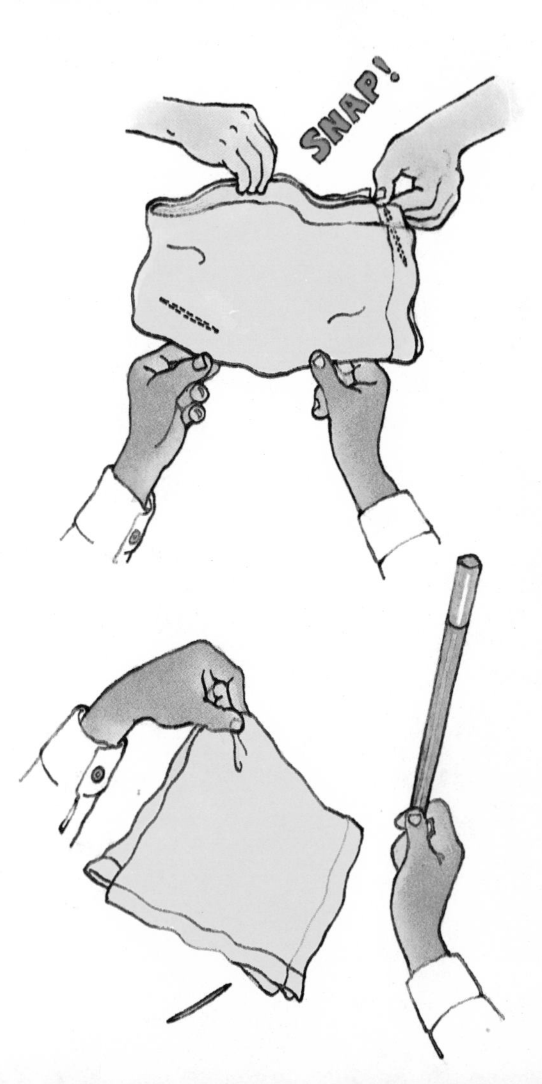

6. Wave a magic wand over the handkerchief. Say, "Abracadabra!" Shake out the handkerchief. The whole toothpick will drop.

Tip: Keep track of the hidden toothpick and be sure this is the one that is broken.

Alice in Wonderland

by Lewis Carroll

Alice was beginning to get very tired of sitting beside her sister on the bank, and of having nothing to do. Once or twice she had peeped into the book her sister was reading, but it had no pictures or conversations in it. "And what is the use of a book," thought Alice, "without pictures or conversations?"

So she was deciding (as well as she could, for the hot day made her feel very, very sleepy), whether the pleasure of making a daisy chain would be worth the trouble of getting up and picking the daisies. Suddenly a White Rabbit with pink eyes ran close by her.

There was nothing so very remarkable in that. And Alice did not think it so very much out of the way to hear the Rabbit say to itself, "Oh dear! Oh dear! I shall be too late!" (When she thought it over afterwards, it seemed that she ought to have wondered at this, but at the time it all seemed quite natural.) But, when the Rabbit actually took a watch out of its waistcoat pocket, and looked at it, and then hurried on, Alice started to her feet. It flashed across her mind that she had never before seen

a rabbit with either a waistcoat pocket, or a watch to take out of it. And, burning with curiosity, she ran very quickly across the field after it, and was just in time to see the Rabbit pop down a large rabbit hole under the hedge.

In another moment down went Alice after it, never once thinking how in the world she was to get out again.

The rabbit hole went straight on like a tunnel for some way. Then it dipped suddenly down, so suddenly that Alice had not a moment to think about stopping herself before she found herself falling down what seemed to be a very deep well.

The Long Fall

Either the well was very deep, or she fell very slowly, for she had plenty of time as she was falling to look about her, and to wonder what was going to happen next. First, she tried to look down and make out what she was coming to, but it was too dark to see anything. Then she looked at the sides of the well, and noticed that they were filled with cupboards and bookshelves. Here and there she saw maps and pictures hung upon pegs. She took down a jar from one of the shelves as she passed. It was labeled "ORANGE MARMALADE," but to her great disappointment it was empty. She did not want to drop the jar, for fear of killing somebody underneath. She managed, however, to put it into one of the cupboards as she fell past it.

"Well!" thought Alice to herself. "After such a fall as this, I shall think nothing of tumbling downstairs! How brave they'll all think me at home! Why, I wouldn't say anything about it, even if I fell off the top of the house!"

Down, down, down. Would the fall never come to an end? "I wonder how many miles I've

fallen by this time?" she said aloud. "I must be getting somewhere near the center of the earth. Let me see: that would be four thousand miles down, I think." (You see, Alice had learned several things of this sort in her lessons in the schoolroom. This was not a very good time or place for showing off though, for there was no one to listen to her. Yet it was good practice to say it over.) "Yes, that's about the right distance."

Presently she began again. "I wonder if I shall fall right through the earth! How funny it'll seem to come out among the people who walk with their heads downwards!—But I shall have to ask them what the name of the country is, you know. Please, Ma'am, is this New Zealand? Or Australia? And what an ignorant little girl they'll think me for asking! No, it'll never do to ask. Perhaps I shall see it written somewhere."

Down, down, down. There was nothing else to do. So Alice soon began talking again. "Dinah'll miss me very much tonight, I should think!" Dinah was the cat. "I hope they'll remember her saucer of milk at tea time.

Dinah, my dear! I wish you were down here with me! There are no mice in the air, I'm afraid, but you might catch a bat, and that's very like a mouse, you know. But do cats eat bats, I wonder?" And here Alice began to get rather sleepy, and went on saying to herself, in a dreamy sort of way, "Do cats eat bats? Do cats eat bats?" and sometimes, "Do bats eat cats?" for, you see, since she couldn't answer either question, it didn't much matter which way she put it. She felt that she was dozing off. She had just begun to dream that she was walking hand in hand with Dinah. She was saying to her, very seriously, "Now, Dinah, tell me the truth. Did you ever eat a bat?" Suddenly, thump! thump! Down she came upon a heap of sticks and dry leaves.

The White Rabbit Again

Alice was not a bit hurt, and she jumped to her feet in a moment. She looked up, but it was all dark overhead. Before her was another long passage, and the White Rabbit was still in sight, hurrying down it. There was not a moment to be lost. Away went Alice like the wind, and was just in time to hear the Rabbit say, as it turned a corner, "Oh my ears and whiskers, how late it's getting!" She was close behind it when she turned the corner, but the Rabbit was no longer to be seen. She found herself in a long, low hall, which was lit up by a row of lamps hanging from the roof.

There were doors all around the hall, but they were all locked. When Alice had been all the way down one side and up the other, trying every door, she walked sadly down the middle, wondering how she was ever to get out again.

Suddenly she came upon a little three-legged table, all made of solid glass. There was nothing on it but a tiny golden key, and Alice's first idea was that this might belong to one of the doors of the hall. But, either the locks were too large, or the key was too small, for it would not open any of them. However, on the second time around, she came upon a low curtain she had not noticed before, and behind it was a little door about fifteen inches high. She tried the little golden key in the lock, and to her great delight it fit!

Alice opened the door and found that it led into a small passage, not much larger than a rat hole. She knelt down and looked along the passage into the loveliest garden you ever saw.

How she longed to get out of that dark hall, and walk among those beds of bright flowers and those cool fountains. But she could not even get her head through the doorway. "And even if my head would go through," thought poor Alice, "it would be of very little use without my shoulders. Oh, how I wish I could shut up like a telescope! I think I could, if I only knew how to begin." For, you see, so many strange things had happened, that Alice had begun to think very few things impossible.

There seemed to be no use in waiting by the little door. She went back to the table, half hoping she might find another key on it, or at any rate a book of rules for making people like telescopes. This time she found a little bottle on it ("which certainly was not here before," said Alice). Tied around the neck of the bottle was a paper label, with the words "DRINK ME" beautifully printed on it in large letters.

It was all very well to say "Drink Me," but the wise little Alice was not going to do that in a hurry. "No, I'll look first," she said, "and see whether it's marked 'poison' or not." She had read several nice little stories about children who had got burned, and eaten up by wild beasts, and other unpleasant things, all because they would not remember the simple rules their friends had taught them. But Alice did remember the rules she had learned. She knew that a red-hot poker will burn you if you hold it too long; and that, if you cut your finger very deeply with a knife, it usually bleeds. And she also never would forget that, if you drink from a bottle marked "poison," it is almost certain to be harmful for you sooner or later.

However, this bottle was not marked "poison." Alice decided to taste it. She found it delicious. (It had, in fact, a sort of mixed flavor

of cherry tart, custard, pineapple, roast turkey, toffy, and hot buttered toast.) She very soon finished the whole bottle off.

"What a strange feeling!" said Alice. "I must be shutting up like a telescope!"

And so she was. She was now only ten inches tall, and her face brightened up, for she would now be the right size for going through the little door into the lovely garden. First, however, she waited for a few minutes to see if she was going to shrink any further. She felt a little nervous about this. "For it might end, you know," said Alice to herself, "in my going out altogether, like a candle. I wonder what I should be like then?" And she tried to imagine what the flame of a candle looks like after the candle is blown out, for she could not remember having seen such a thing.

After a while, finding that nothing more happened, she decided to go into the garden at once. But, poor Alice! When she got to the door, she found she had forgotten the little golden key, and when she went back to the table for it, she found she could not possibly reach it. She could see it quite plainly through the glass,

and she tried her best to climb up one of the legs of the table, but it was too slippery. And when she had tired herself out with trying, the poor little thing sat down and cried.

"Come, there's no use in crying like that!" said Alice to herself rather sharply. "I tell you to stop this minute!" She usually gave herself very good advice (though she very seldom followed it), and sometimes she scolded herself so hard that she brought tears to her eyes. Once she remembered trying to box her own ears for having cheated herself in a game she was playing against herself, for this strange child was very fond of pretending to be two people. "But it's no use now," thought Alice, "to pretend to be two people! There's hardly enough of me left to make one nice person!"

Soon she saw a little glass box that was lying under the table. She opened it, and in it she found a very small cake, on which the words "EAT ME!" were beautifully marked in raisins. "Well, I'll eat it," said Alice, "and if it makes me grow larger, I will be able to reach the key. And if it makes me grow smaller, I can creep under the door. So either way I'll get into the garden, and I don't care which happens!"

She ate a little bit, and said to herself, "Which way? Which way?" holding her hand on top of her head to feel which way it was growing. She was quite surprised to find that she stayed the same size. To be sure, this is what usually happens when one eats cake. Alice had got so used to new things happening that it seemed quite dull for life to go on in the normal way.

So she set to work, and very soon finished off the cake.

"Curiouser and curiouser!" cried Alice. (She was so much surprised, that for the moment she quite forgot how to speak good English.) "Now I'm opening out like the largest telescope that ever was! Good-bye, feet!" (For when she looked down at her feet, they seemed to be almost out of sight, they were getting so far off.) "Oh, my poor little feet, I wonder who will put on your shoes and stockings for you now, dears? I'm sure I shall not be able! I shall be much too far off to trouble myself about you. You must manage the best way you can—but I must be kind to them," thought Alice, "or perhaps they won't walk the way I want to go! Let me see. I'll give them a new pair of boots every Christmas."

And she went on planning to herself how she would manage it. "They must go by the postman," she thought. "How funny it will seem, sending presents to one's own feet!"

Alice's Right Foot
Hearthrug, near the Fender
(with Alice's love).

"Oh dear, what nonsense I'm talking!"

Just at this moment her head struck against the roof of the hall. In fact, she was now more than nine feet high, and she at once took up the little golden key and hurried off to the garden door.

Poor Alice! It was as much as she could do to look into the garden with one eye. To get through was more hopeless than ever. She sat down and began to cry again.

"You ought to be ashamed of yourself," said Alice, "a big girl like you," (wasn't it true?) "to go on crying in this way! Stop this moment, I tell you!" But she went on all the same, crying gallons of tears, until there was a large pool all around her, reaching halfway down the hall.

The Pool of Tears

After a time she heard a little tapping of feet in the distance, and she hastily dried her eyes to see what was coming. It was the White Rabbit returning, handsomely dressed, with a pair of white kid gloves in one hand and a large fan in the other. He came hopping along in a great hurry, saying to himself, as he came, "Oh! The Duchess, the Duchess! Oh! Won't she be angry if I have kept her waiting!" Alice felt so upset that she was ready to ask help of anyone. So, when the Rabbit came near her, she began in a low, timid voice, "If you please, Sir—" The Rabbit jumped up, dropped the white kid gloves and the fan, and hurried away as fast as he could go.

Alice picked up the fan and gloves. She was very hot in the hall, so she kept fanning herself all the time she went on talking. "Dear, dear! How strange everything is today! And yesterday things went on just as usual. I wonder if I've been changed in the night! I can almost remember feeling a little different this morning. But if I'm not the same, who in the world am I? Ah, that's the great puzzle!" And she began thinking over all the children she knew to see if she could have been changed for any of them.

"I'm sure I'm not Ada," she said, "for her hair goes in such long ringlets, and mine isn't curly at all. And I'm sure I can't be Mabel. Besides she's she, and I'm I, and—oh dear, how puzzling it all is!"

As she said this she looked down at her hands, and was surprised to see that she had put on one of the Rabbit's little white kid gloves while she was talking. "How can I have done that?" she thought. "I must be growing small again." She got up and went to the table to measure herself by it, and found that, as nearly as she could guess, she was now about two feet high, and was continuing to shrink rapidly. She soon found out that the cause of this was the fan she was holding, and she dropped it hastily, just in time to save herself from shrinking away altogether.

"That was a narrow escape!" said Alice, a good deal frightened at the sudden change, but very glad to find herself still there. And she ran with all speed back to the little door. But,

alas! The little door was shut again and the little golden key was lying on the glass table as before. "And things are worse than ever," thought the poor child, "for I never was so small as this before, never! And I guess it's too bad, that it is!"

As she said these words her foot slipped, and in another moment, splash! She was up to her chin in salt water. Her first idea was that she had somehow fallen into the sea, "and in that case I can go back by train," she said to herself. (Alice had been to the seashore once in her life. She had decided that wherever you go along the seashore, you find a number of boats in the sea, children digging in the sand with wooden spades, then a row of cabins, and behind them a railroad station.) However, she soon discovered that she was in a pool of tears which she had wept when she was nine feet high.

"I wish I hadn't cried so much!" said Alice, as she swam about, trying to find her way out. "I shall be punished for it now, I suppose, by being drowned in my own tears! That will be a strange thing, to be sure! However, everything is strange today."

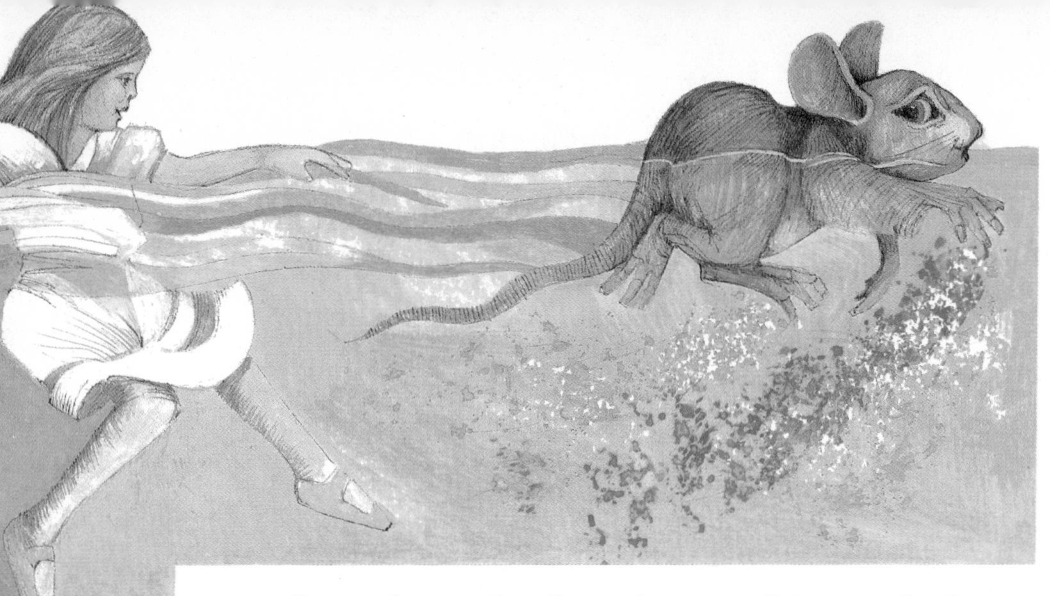

Just then she heard something splashing about in the pool a little way off, and she swam nearer to see what it was. At first, she thought it must be a walrus or hippopotamus, but then she remembered how small she was now. She soon discovered that it was only a mouse, that had slipped in like herself.

"Would it be of any use, now," thought Alice, "to speak to this mouse? Everything is so strange down here, that I should think very likely it can talk. At any rate, there's no harm in trying." So she began: "O Mouse, do you know the way out of this pool? I am very tired of swimming about here, O Mouse!" (Alice thought this must be the right way of speaking to a mouse. She had never done such a thing before, but she remembered having seen, in her brother's Latin book, "A mouse—of a mouse—to a mouse—a mouse—O mouse!") The Mouse looked at her rather curiously, and seemed to wink at her with one of its little eyes, but it said nothing.

"Perhaps it doesn't understand English," thought Alice. "I dare say it's a French mouse." So she began again, *"Où est ma chatte?"* which was the first sentence in her French book. It means, "Where is my cat?" The mouse gave a sudden leap out of the water, and seemed to shake all over with fright. "Oh, I beg your pardon!" cried Alice, afraid that she had hurt the poor animal's feelings. "I quite forgot that you didn't like cats."

"Not like cats!" cried the Mouse in a shrill voice. "Would you like cats, if you were me?"

"Well, perhaps not," said Alice in a calm tone; "don't be angry about it. And yet I wish I could show you our cat, Dinah. I think you'd like cats if you could only see her. She is such a dear quiet thing," Alice went on, half to herself, as she swam about the pool. "She sits purring so nicely by the fire, licking her paws and washing her face—and she is such a nice soft thing to nurse—and she's such a fine one for catching mice—Oh, I beg your pardon!" cried Alice again. This time the Mouse was shaking all over, and she felt sure it must be really worried. "We won't talk about her any more, if you'd rather not."

"We, indeed!" cried the Mouse, who was shaking down to the end of its tail. "As if I would talk on such a subject! Our family always hated cats. Nasty, mean, ugly things! Don't let me hear the name again!"

"I won't, indeed!" said Alice, in a great hurry to change the subject of the conversation. "Are you—are you fond—of—dogs?" The Mouse did not answer, so Alice went on eagerly. "There is such a nice little dog near our house I should like to show you! A little bright-eyed terrier, you know, with, oh, such long curly brown hair! And it'll fetch things when you throw them, and it'll sit up and beg for its dinner. It'll do all sorts of things. I can't remember half of them. It belongs to a farmer, you know, and he says it's so useful, it's worth a hundred dollars! He says it kills all the rats and—oh dear!" cried Alice in a sorrowful tone. "I'm afraid I've

hurt its feelings again!" For the Mouse was swimming away from her as hard as it could go, and making quite a commotion in the pool.

So she called softly after it, "Mouse dear! Do come back again, and we won't talk about cats, or dogs either, if you don't like them!" When the Mouse heard this, it turned around and swam slowly back to her. Its face was quite pale (with anger, Alice thought), and it said in a low trembling voice, "Let us get to shore; then I'll tell you why I hate cats and dogs."

It was time to leave the pool, for it had become crowded with the birds and animals

that had fallen into it. There was a Duck, a Dodo, an Eaglet, and several other odd creatures. Alice led the way, and the whole party swam to the shore.

After Alice heard the Mouse's sad story, she had many more strange adventures in a world where nothing seemed to go the way it would go in the real world. It was a good while—and many adventures—before she returned safely to her home and family. But she did get back, finally, none the worse for her strange experiences.

The Falling Star

I saw a star slide down the sky,
Blinding the north as it went by,
Too burning and too quick to hold,
Too lovely to be bought or sold,
Good only to make wishes on
And then forever to be gone.

—Sara Teasdale

UNIT FIVE

Promising Places

Dr. Frankenstein and Friends

by Val R. Cheatham

Cast

Dr. Frankenstein, *evil scientific genius*

Igor, *his assistant, unable to speak*

Wolfman, *werewolf*

Dracula, *Count of Transylvania*

Vampira, *who wants to be alone*

Tombstone, *who is looking for a grave*

Happy Medium, *fortune-teller*

Boy

First Girl

Second Girl

Other children, extras

Time

Late at night

Setting

Gloomy room in a haunted house belonging to Dr. Frankenstein. Sounds of wind, thunder, and heavy rain are heard from offstage.

At Rise of Curtain

Door creaks as DR. FRANKENSTEIN enters, taking off his hat and coat.

DR. FRANKENSTEIN: Igor! Igor! *(IGOR enters, walking slightly bent over.)* What a terrible, dark, and stormy night! *(Both look out the window.)* Beautiful, isn't it?

IGOR: *(moves about, grunting and laughing)*

DR. FRANKENSTEIN *(hands his coat and hat to IGOR):* Tell me, Igor, have any of my guests arrived?

IGOR: *(shakes his head "no" and laughs while he hangs up the coat)*

DR. FRANKENSTEIN: No? This is most unusual! My invitation read twelve o'clock midnight. *(He looks at his pocketwatch. A knock is heard. IGOR starts for the door. But before he gets there, DRACULA comes in, holding his cape like wings.)*

DRACULA: Good e-e-e-evening!

DR. FRANKENSTEIN: Ah, Count Dracula, I'm so pleased you could come. *(shakes DRACULA's hand)*

DRACULA *(clicks his heels, bows slightly, then takes DR. FRANKENSTEIN's hand, examines it with interest):* My pleasure. You are like a relative to me. A blood relative. *(He lifts cape and tries to put it over DR. FRANKENSTEIN's head. DR. FRANKENSTEIN backs away.)*

DR. FRANKENSTEIN: No, no, no, no, stop!

IGOR: *(laughs and moves behind DRACULA to take his cape)*

DRACULA *(turns to look at IGOR, then speaks to DR. FRANKENSTEIN):* I see you are still experimenting, Dr. Frankenstein.

DR. FRANKENSTEIN: Oh, no! Igor is my assistant. He is not an experiment. *(IGOR reaches for DRACULA's cape.)* No, no, Igor! Down! Down! Count Dracula never removes his cape.

IGOR: *(laughs and moves to the opposite side of the stage)*

DRACULA *(smooths cape):* Your note said to come at midnight. It said there would be others. *(looks around room)*

DR. FRANKENSTEIN: Yes. *(checks watch again)* I don't understand why they are not here! *(Suddenly WOLFMAN rushes in through window. He moves toward DRACULA.)*

DRACULA *(raises his arm):* Stop, stop, you beast! One step nearer and I'll bite your neck.

WOLFMAN *(stops):* Ah, heck. Weren't you scared? Didn't I frighten anyone? *(looks around)* How about you, Doctor? Were you scared?

DR. FRANKENSTEIN: It was an impressive try.

WOLFMAN *(to IGOR):* How about you? Were you scared?

IGOR: *(moves about, clapping hands and laughing)*

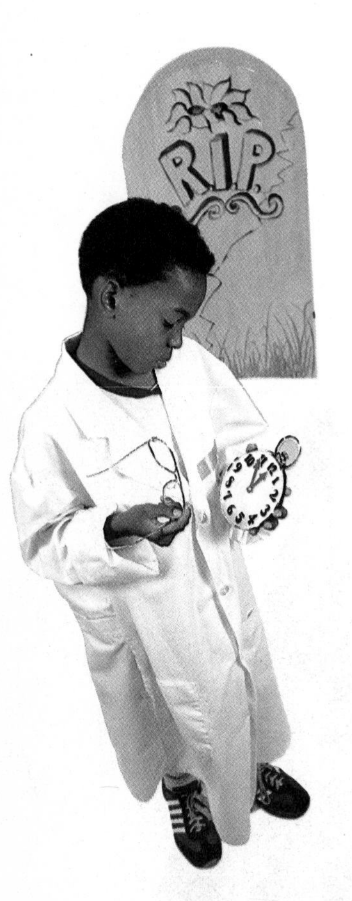

WOLFMAN *(moving away from IGOR):* I see you're still working on experiments in that laboratory of yours, Doctor. *(From offstage, the voice of TOMBSTONE is heard speaking very softly.)*

TOMBSTONE *(offstage):* Hark! Death is calling!

DR. FRANKENSTEIN: Igor, Tombstone has arrived! *(IGOR opens the door.)*

TOMBSTONE *(entering slowly):* You have someone who needs me?

DR. FRANKENSTEIN *(moving closer to shake hands):* Tombstone, I'm so happy you could come. *(No hand is available, leaving DR. FRANKENSTEIN in an awkward position.)*

TOMBSTONE: Just pat my R.I.P. *(DR. FRANKENSTEIN does so.)* Ah-h-h-h.

DR. FRANKENSTEIN: *(introduces guests):* Tombstone, I believe you know Count Dracula and Wolfman. *(DRACULA gives a slight bow and a click of heels. WOLFMAN snarls.)*

TOMBSTONE: Yes, I know them very well. Now, Doctor, explain why you invited us here.

DR. FRANKENSTEIN: Patience, my dear Tombstone, patience. There are still more to come.

HAPPY MEDIUM *(offstage, in crackling voice):* Heh, heh, heh! *(throws open door)* Don't be waiting for me, dearies. *(steps inside, followed by VAMPIRA)* We're both here and my crystal ball says we're right on time.

DRACULA: How would you know? That crystal ball is as useless as a piece of rock.

DR. FRANKENSTEIN: Friends, please—we are not here to insult each other. We have a very serious matter to discuss. *(to HAPPY MEDIUM and VAMPIRA)* Please come in, come in.

VAMPIRA *(slowly moves to far corner):* I vant to be alone.

DR. FRANKENSTEIN *(holds up hands for attention):* We are all here now. Please listen. Each of us in this room faces a terrible problem: No one is frightened of us anymore. (All protest at once.)

DRACULA: Lies, all lies!

IGOR: *(moves around, shaking head, with angry sounds)*

WOLFMAN: *(growls and snarls)*

TOMBSTONE: No, no, it isn't true!

HAPPY MEDIUM: You're wrong, wrong, you hear!

DR. FRANKENSTEIN *(shouting):* Stop! *(All become quiet.)* Protest all you like, but deep down you know it is true! No one is frightened of us anymore. *(He looks at each of them in turn.)* Well? *(pointing to WOLFMAN)* When was the last time people screamed in terror and fled for their lives when they saw you?

WOLFMAN: Oh, heck. I might as well tell you. Since they started showing late movies on TV, hardly anyone ever comes out at night. But . . . but, I did scare a lady in the park the other day during lunch. *(kicks at floor)* Of course it was only because she thought I was a dog, trying to eat her sandwich. And I don't even like tuna fish!

DR. FRANKENSTEIN *(to DRACULA):* And how about you, my dear Count? When last did you scare someone?

DRACULA: Too long ago! They imitate me on TV commercials, and now, every time I speak, people laugh. *(looks at audience)* Can you imagine? They laugh!

DR. FRANKENSTEIN *(to TOMBSTONE):* And how about you, Tombstone? Do people scream in terror when they see you?

TOMBSTONE: No, they don't. It's very sad. I can hardly stand it anymore. *(Sobs)*

DR. FRANKENSTEIN: There, there. *(comforts TOMBSTONE)* Things may look more gloomy tomorrow. *(turns to HAPPY MEDIUM)* When you predict the future, Happy Medium, do people believe you?

HAPPY MEDIUM: I guess I might as well confess. Business is off. I don't have any customers. These days, when I offer to look into the crystal ball and tell people their future, they say, "Forget it. I saw that stunt on TV last week." And then they walk away.

DR. FRANKENSTEIN: My fellow monsters, this is our problem: TV! *(to WOLFMAN)* It keeps people home at night. *(to DRACULA)* It shows you as a joke. *(to TOMBSTONE)* And you as a silly superstition. *(to*

HAPPY MEDIUM) And you as a busybody who guesses at the future!

HAPPY MEDIUM *(angrily):* Busybody? Guesses at the future?

DRACULA *(to audience):* Well, perhaps there is some truth in TV, after all!

DR. FRANKENSTEIN: And even I, Dr. Frankenstein, the great evil genius, who made the world's greatest monster! In cartoons, I'm a madman whose monster goes around *helping* others. Disgusting! *(turns to VAMPIRA)* And Vampira, our beautiful and evil Vampira! We see her in shampoo commercials.

VAMPIRA: I just vant to be alone.

DR. FRANKENSTEIN: Needless to say, if TV continues to influence people, we will all be alone—very much alone!

DRACULA: Yes! I wish they would do away with TV and just have movies. They knew how to show me as a frightening beast!

DR. FRANKENSTEIN: Then what is the answer to our problem?

HAPPY MEDIUM: Let me look into the crystal ball and find out.

DRACULA: Put away that useless piece of junk and help us think. *(A knock is heard.)*

TOMBSTONE: Hark! Someone is coming in.

DR. FRANKENSTEIN: Shh! Keep still! Don't move! *(All grow quiet and stand still.)*

BOY *(opening door, which creaks; timidly):* Hello? *(enters, followed by GIRLS)* Anyone home?

FIRST GIRL: I hope the owner doesn't mind. It's raining too hard to stay outdoors. *(calling)* Come on, everybody. *(OTHER CHILDREN enter very cautiously.)*

BOY *(seeing TOMBSTONE; frightened):* Hey! What is this place, anyway?

SECOND GIRL *(seeing DRACULA):* Look! Dracula! *(nervously)* He looks real enough

to bite me. I'm scared. Look at all these monsters!

BOY: That's what it is—a wax museum of monsters. *(points to DR. FRANKENSTEIN)* Dr. Frankenstein! I saw the late movie on TV the other night in which he made his monster. It was really scary!

FIRST GIRL: That werewolf gives me the shivers.

BOY: This is a terrifying wax museum. I'd like to come back—only in broad daylight.

SECOND GIRL: Me, too. Right now, let's get out of here. I'd rather be outside—storm or no storm. *(starts for door)*

OTHER CHILDREN *(ad lib):* I'm leaving! This place gives me the creeps! It's too scary! *(CHILDREN exit.)*

DR. FRANKENSTEIN: Did you hear that? He said my monster was terrible!

WOLFMAN: And I gave them the shivers. Gee whiz! *(snarls a little)* Just like old times!

DRACULA: The girl thought I would bite her neck. I like it! I like it!

HAPPY MEDIUM: They thought they were in a wax museum. Imagine that—a wax museum. The boy said he would come back when we're open. I wonder if he would. *(looks at crystal ball with puzzled expression)*

VAMPIRA *(from her corner):* Do you think people would pay to see us?

DR. FRANKENSTEIN: That's the answer! Turn this haunted house into a wax museum. People won't watch TV anymore.

TOMBSTONE: We could charge admission. Frighten people and make money, too.

DRACULA: I could buy a new old castle in Transylvania. I like it! I like it!

WOLFMAN: I could sell tickets . . . that is, if there's a full moon.

HAPPY MEDIUM: I could set up a booth and tell fortunes to the people waiting in line.

DR. FRANKENSTEIN: I could give guided tours of my laboratory. And Igor could sell souvenirs. *(chuckles loudly)*

VAMPIRA: Suddenly I don't vant to be alone anymore.

DRACULA: I like it! I like it! *(All move about, rearranging furniture and talking excitedly.)*

IGOR: *(moves to front stage, laughing, and holds up sign reading "The End." Curtain.)*

Angry

Sometimes when the day is bad
And someone's made me very mad
Or I've been given angry stares,
I go behind the front porch stairs.

There, curled up with chin on knee,
I like to be alone with me
And listen to the people talk
And hurry by me on the walk.

There I sit without a sound,
And draw stick pictures on the ground.
If I should tire of it all,
I throw some pebbles at the wall.

After I've been there awhile
And find that I can almost smile,
I brush me off and count to ten
And try to start the day again.

—Marci Ridlon

The Applegates Visit Colorado

by Charles C. Walcutt

One April evening, the Applegate family was having dinner. Freddie looked up from his clam chowder and said, "I can't wait until we can dig our own clams at the beach."

His mother and father looked at each other and smiled. "This summer," said his mother, "is going to be different. I have to attend a convention in Denver, Colorado, and we've decided to plan a family trip around it. We'll arrive in Denver early. Then there will be time for exploring the Rocky Mountains."

"Colorado!" said Freddie's sister, Judy.

"It sounds great, Mother!" said Freddie. "How will we get there?"

"We'll drive."

On a sunny morning in July, the Applegates left their home in Salem and headed west. They drove across Massachusetts, where gardens were blooming. That afternoon, they reached the Hudson River and the Catskill Mountains.

Freddie and Judy asked so many questions that it was never quiet in the car. They asked how wide the Delaware River was and where it went. Then the family turned farther south. They passed through some coal-mining towns in Pennsylvania until they reached the turnpike.

In the next few days, the Applegate family drove on the turnpikes of Pennsylvania, Ohio, Indiana, and Illinois. They saw miles and

miles of cornfields. They crossed the Mississippi River and soon came to the Great Plains. Now, the State of Kansas, they had been told, was one continuous wheatfield. As they passed through a small town, they could see a tall, snowy-white tower in the distance. It looked so strange that they could not believe their eyes.

Judy cried, "Look, Mother, what is that white thing so far away?"

"It looks like a tower, Judy. But why would it be there all by itself?" said her mother.

As they came closer, they saw that it was in a little town. Mrs. Applegate said, "Now I know what it is. It is a grain elevator. That's what they call it. It is used to store the wheat. If it is kept clean and dry, wheat will stay good for a long time—for years."

From then on everybody was watching to see the white towers in the distance. Sometimes there were several of them in a row, and then they knew they were approaching a larger town.

Freddie, who was very hot, although it was only early summer, now noticed that his mother had a puzzled expression on her face. She was gazing out of the car, looking closely at the brown land that stretched out flat to the horizon. She was frowning.

Freddie said, "Mother, I know that expression of yours. You are thinking about a question, but you are also thinking that you don't have an answer to it. For an old asker of questions, that is a problem!"

Mrs. Applegate turned, with a pleased smile. She loved to have her children notice things and think about them. "You're right, Freddie, I'm wondering where the wheat is! It seems to me that it has all been cut, or that it hasn't grown at all. I don't know. After all, it's only the second week in July."

Freddie frowned and looked very carefully at the ground. He saw what looked like little

blades of grass, standing straight up two or three inches from the ground. However, the car was going fast and he could not be sure.

But Mr. Applegate, driving the car, was also smiling to himself. "I have the answer," he said, "and while you have been staring out at the fields beside the road, I have seen something ahead, in the distance, that will surprise you even more. No, perhaps, it will give you the answer. Look!"

By this time it was afternoon, and the Applegate family had been driving across Kansas since early morning. It was bright, and still, and scorching hot. Ahead of the car, the sun beat down on the black road so fiercely that it made the air seem to squirm and dance over the pavement. And often, as they came toward the top of a gradual slope (there were no hills), there seemed to be water in the road, but this vanished as they came closer to it. Now, through the hot, squirming air, in the distance, they saw what looked like a stream of brown water shooting into the air like a brown spray.

As they drove closer they saw something under the brown stream. It was a huge machine, with wheels, and platforms, and belts, and pulleys. "There," said Mr. Applegate, "is a great combine harvester. See, it cuts the wheat, gathers it up, and threshes it."

"What is 'threshes'?" asked Judy, who was very interested in the machine. They stopped by the side of the road to watch.

"Thresh—that's what you do to separate the little grains of wheat from the rest of the plant. The little grains grow at the top of the stalk, and they are surrounded by soft, feathery, fluffy stuff. This has to be separated from the hard grains of wheat. It is called chaff, and that is what you see blowing out of that hole in the machine, into the air."

"What happens to the grains of wheat?" asked Freddie.

"They are stored in a big grain tank on the machine. Later, the harvester dumps the grain into trucks, which take it into the grain elevators."

"Why had they already harvested the wheat we saw earlier?" asked Freddie. "The short brown grass is what is left after the wheat has been cut, isn't it?"

"Yes, Freddie, it is," answered Mr. Applegate. "All of the wheat is not ready to be harvested at the same time. The harvest normally begins in the southeastern part of Kansas. I think there is a difference in the weather of about two weeks between southeastern Kansas and the northwestern end. And did you know that the land is gently rising as we travel west? The change is so gradual that you can't really notice it."

"The altitude will be even higher in the Rockies, won't it, Daddy?" asked Judy.

"Yes, Judy, and I think it's time we continued our trip." Mr. Applegate started the car again. The family drove on toward the Rocky Mountains and the setting sun.

A Scientific Discussion

Everything the Applegates saw raised questions. When they began to ask each other questions, anything could happen. They might have to stop the car at the side of the road and talk until they had solved everything. They simply could not think about their questions and look at all the countryside at the same time. And there was so much beautiful country to see!

When they had just crossed into Colorado, Freddie said, "The air smells different here."

"Yes," replied his father, "it is different. We have climbed until now we are about four thousand feet above sea level, and the air is thinner."

"It doesn't seem any thinner to me," said Judy. "How can we prove that it is?"

Mrs. Applegate now laughed. "Aren't we becoming scientific! Proof for everything, now. Well, I'll tell you how you can prove it. If you just try running up the road, good and fast, you will be surprised at how soon you are out of breath."

"Let's stop up the road a way, at the next service station. We need gasoline."

When they stopped, in a few minutes, Judy and Freddie had a short race beside the road. Sure enough, they found that they could fill their lungs very easily, but there did not seem to be very much air in them when they were filled. They were both soon out of breath.

Judy said, "Nobody could run very far here!"

Her father answered, "Yes, they can. People who live here don't get out of breath any sooner than we do at home."

"Will I get used to it soon?" she asked.

"Yes, you will, after we've stayed this high above sea level for a while. But you will be very sleepy for the first few days."

"I'm not sleepy now, Daddy."

"Perhaps we're not high enough yet," said Mr. Applegate. "Wait until we reach the top of the Rocky Mountains. Then we will be more than twelve thousand feet above sea level. That's three times as high as we are now."

Soon they were driving across dusty plains. The farther they went, the more clearly they could see that they were climbing. The land became rough and rocky and dry.

In the distance lay the Rocky Mountains. It was hard to tell where the clouds stopped and the snow-topped mountains began.

The next day they rode up the side of the great mountain. After they passed a high, curving rock, they could see a small lake with large pieces of ice floating in it.

"Look, icebergs!" cried Freddie. "Maybe there's a glacier somewhere near here."

"I don't believe that this is from a glacier, Freddie," said Mrs. Applegate. "It looks as if it came down off those rocks up there," and she pointed to the rocky side of the mountain, where the snow seemed to be packed into ice.

Judy said, "Daddy, could we stop and look?" Mr. Applegate stopped the car, and Judy jumped out and ran down toward the water. The ground was muddy and rough, and in a minute she was panting for breath. In another minute she had a nosebleed, and she looked back at her brother and parents in alarm. "Daddy, Daddy, what's the matter with me?" She came running back toward the car.

Mrs. Applegate tipped Judy's head back and wiped her face. "It's all right, dear. It's the altitude. Up here the air is thin, and you are likely to have a nosebleed if you run too hard. It will stop in a minute." And it did.

Back in the car, Freddie looked at the lake. It was the bluest water he had ever seen. It was bluer than the Atlantic Ocean near his home in Salem, Massachusetts, bluer than anything he could think of. But instead of saying something about the blue lake, he asked a question. "Why do people have nose-bleeds because of the altitude, Mother?"

"That's difficult to explain, but I'll try. Did you know that the air around us has weight? It presses against the earth. It weighs about fifteen pounds per square inch."

"Fifteen pounds per square inch. What does *that* mean?" said Freddie.

"It means that on any spot that is an inch square, there is a column of air pressing down with a weight of fifteen pounds. But that is at sea level. That's the way it is in Salem, which is by the sea."

"Mother," said Freddie, "do you mean I'm carrying that weight of air on my shoulders all the time?" Freddie had a picture in his mind of a lot of columns of air, like long square sticks,

touching his head and shoulders and reaching up into the air. "How far up into the sky do these columns of air go?"

"Well, Freddie, they're not separate columns or sticks of air. It's just all the air, and to measure its weight or pressure you have to say what it weighs on a certain definite amount of land—or person."

"But, Mother, I don't feel such a weight on my shoulders. Why, fifteen pounds is a lot of weight. How could I carry all that on every square inch of my shoulders? And what if I lie on my back? Would there be more air weighing down on me then? And why is it that I don't feel any different when I go indoors, where there is a roof to protect me from all that heavy air?"

Mrs. Applegate exploded with a gay laugh. She bent over and held her face in her hands while she laughed. "Freddie, you do ask the most wonderful questions! They are all good questions, too. The answer is that air, which goes up a very long way above the earth, presses on everything from all sides at once, not just on top.

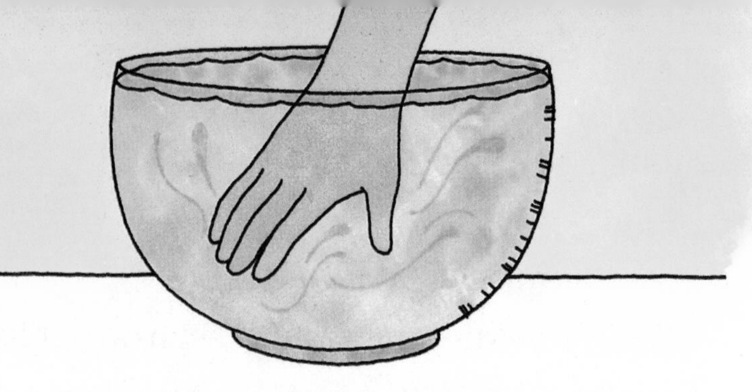

"If you put your hand down deep into some water, or swim down deep in a pool, you can feel the water pressing on you all over your body. Air is the same, except that it doesn't press so hard, and since we live in it all the time we are used to it and don't feel it at all. But if all the air were taken away—that is, if you were put in a vacuum where there was no air at all—you would explode, because there is the same pressure in your body, pushing out, as there is air pressure pushing in. So you see, the roof doesn't make any difference at all.

"And now we can explain why Judy had a nosebleed. The higher above the sea you climb, the less the weight of the air. Up here we are nearly ten thousand feet above the level of the sea; that's nearly two miles. And so there is less air pressing down on us from above. The pressure inside Judy became greater than the pressure of the air on her from the outside. A tiny vein in her nose broke, and the blood rushed out. That's the whole story. Any more questions?"

"Yes," said Judy, whose nose had stopped bleeding, "I want to know why I'm the only one to have a nosebleed!"

"Perhaps," said Mr. Applegate with a laugh, "because you are smaller, your skin is a little thinner than ours, and so it isn't quite so strong as ours. Or perhaps it's because you were running, and that made your heart beat faster and pump the blood harder. I'm not really sure. Some people have nosebleeds, and some don't. I don't think you will have any more nosebleeds, Judy."

"Well," said Judy, and now she laughed at herself, "first one problem and then another. Now I'm so sleepy I can hardly keep my eyes open!"

"I'm sleepy, too," said Freddie. "You said we'd be sleepy!" He looked at his father as if it were his fault.

"I did say so, and I'm sleepy, too." Here Mr. Applegate opened his mouth in a great yawn, and a moment later Mrs. Applegate yawned, too. Judy yawned. Freddie yawned.

"I think it's time for a nap," said Mrs. Applegate, and so they drew off to the side of the road, under the sweet-smelling pine trees, and went to sleep with the sound of running water in their ears.

The Ballad of Dan

by Jo Carr

There was a boy—and his name was Dan.
His heart was sad.
He was young
but his thoughts were old,
old and weary, and wondering how
he could manage now.

Dan turned back to look at the flat.
It was just like the others, row on row
of old brick buildings, lined up so,
like domino soldiers, crowded and plain . . .
all but one. It wasn't the same.

The front apartment on the second floor
was *home—his* family name on the door.
It was there he had squabbled with Bob
  and Lou,
there he had practiced his two-times-two
by the light of the bare bulb overhead
after his brothers were both in bed.
There he had eaten a thousand times
and gone to sleep with counting rhymes
still batting around in his funny head,
on the wiggly cot that was his bed.
There he had joked with Mom and Dad—
taken his punishment when he'd been bad—
and it was home—and his—and good.
Dan remembered it well. Now he stood
looking back, and wondering how
the family could manage now.

"There's been a wreck," the officer said.
Dan put his hand on his aching head. . . .
And then he heard they'd be okay.
They were feeling better every day.
When he thought of his parents and Lou
  and Bob,
Dan wanted to help—he would find a job.

He walked for a while, and shifted the pack
so it would lie easier on his back.
Each different street
felt strange and foreign to his feet.
He was out of the part of the city he knew.

And he was hungry.
Dan kept watch as he plodded along
for a hot-dog stand, or a small café,
where a guy could work to earn his pay—
or, if he couldn't . . . well, even so,
he could afford a *little.* You just can't go
walking forever with nothing to eat.

It was two blocks down that he saw the sign
that said "JOE'S EATS"—and that was fine—
because if Joe had Eats, then Dan was the guy
who could sure help eat them!
He skipped a beat,
hurrying down the stranger street
toward the light, and warmth, and a
  friendly face
and something to eat at Joe's fine place!
Dan could smell the onions! He opened the
  door. . . .

But a burly man said, "Hey, you"—
"Get out of here. No kids during school hours."

The man's words were like a slap in the face.
Dan backed out of Joe's place.
He felt hungry and so alone.
His heart was like a hunk of stone—
cold and heavy in his chest.
Dan wouldn't step inside that place again,
even if he did need a friend.

Dan kept walking.
He was hungry and hurt.
All he could think of was the last meal he ate.
The blocks were long. It was getting late.
And Dan was weary. He never knew
he could get so tired. Then the smell of stew—
rich and meaty like Mama's stew—
drifted out of a small café.

Dan sniffed it deep, with half-closed eyes.
A sign in the window said "Homemade Pies."
Dan remembered "JOE'S EATS," and squinted
his eyes. . . .
"Sure would like a bowl of hot stew and
homemade pie,"
he thought as he walked on by.
But the smell of the stew won out at last.
Dan turned back, and looked some more,
and saw a small open door.
He went in, shyly, and stood inside,
embarrassed—so hungry he almost cried—
not knowing what to do or say,
until the man at the counter looked his way.
"Hello, there! Come on in."
The man gave Dan a friendly grin,
and motioned him to a table, too.

He scooped up ice in an amber glass,
filled it with water
and gave Dan a menu to order by.

The man waited for Dan to unwind—
and then in a voice that was gruff but kind,
said, "We make a mighty good stew.
A twenty-cent bowl of that might do—
and a glass of milk. What do you say?"
Dan just nodded, wondering whether to trust
this man.

The man went away,
back to the kitchen to get the stew . . .
and he brought it, too,
and the milk,
and crackers.
Then he brought his coffee, and he sat
down, too,
at the table with Dan—as if he *wanted* to,
so Dan wouldn't have to eat alone.
He talked a little, like Dan was grown—
about the weather, and the price of meat—
and how the pavement hurts your feet
when you have walked for a long, long way.
And the man was kind.
And Dan didn't mind
when he finally asked where Dan was
bound, and where he belonged.

Then Dan found
he needed to talk—and he told the man
about "JOE'S EATS," and his long, long walk.
Dan discovered he could even talk
about the wreck and of his plight.
"Well," said the man,
"How would you like a piece of homemade pie?
I'll have one, too.
And by the way,
I need some help with this café,
afternoons, after school.
What do you say?"

Dan grinned a lopsided grin of his own . . .
"I say, OK!"

Yagua Days

by Cruz Martel

It was raining steadily on the Lower East Side. From the doorway of his parents' **bodega,** Adan Riera watched a car splash the sidewalk.

School had ended for the summer two days ago. And for two days it had rained! Adan wanted to play in East River Park. But with so much rain, about the only thing a boy could do was watch the cars splash by.

---

yagua (jä′ gwä), the outer covering of a palm leaf.
bodega (bō deg′ ä), a Puerto Rican grocery store.

Of course he could help his father. Adan enjoyed working in the bodega. He liked the smells of the fruits and the different colors of the vegetables. But today he would rather be in the park.

Jorge came in, slapping water off his hat. He smiled. "Why the long face, Adan?"

"Rainy days are terrible days."

"No, they're wonderful days. They're yagua days."

"Stop teasing, Jorge. Yesterday you told me the vegetables and fruits in the bodega are grown in trucks. What's a yagua day?"

"This day is a yagua day. And Puerto Rican vegetables and fruits *are* grown in trucks. Why, I have a truck myself. Every day I water it!"

Adan's mother and father came in from the back.

"**Hola,** Jorge. You look wet," said Adan's father.

"I feel wetter. But it's a wonderful feeling. It's a yagua-day feeling!"

His mother and father liked Jorge. They had all grown up together in Puerto Rico.

"So you've been telling Adan about yagua days?"

"**Sí.** Here's a letter for you from **Corral Viejo,** where we all had some of the best yagua days."

Adan's father read the letter. "Good news! My brother Ulise wants Mami, Adan, and me to visit him on his **finca** for two weeks. It's been years since I've been to Puerto Rico," he added thoughtfully.

---

hola (ō′ la), hello.
si (sē), yes.
Corral Viejo (kō rôl′ vē ye′ hō), old corral.
finca (fēn′ kä), plantation.

"Adan's never been there," replied his mother. "We can ask my brother to take care of the bodega. Adan will meet his family in the mountains at last."

Adan clapped his hands. "Puerto Rico! Who cares about the rain!"

Jorge smiled. "Maybe you'll even have a few yagua days. **Hasta luego. Y que gocen mucho!**"

---

hasta luego (ä′stä lü we′gō), till we meet again; good-bye.
y que gocen mucho (ē ke gō′sen mü′chō), and have fun!

Tío Ulise met them at the airport in **Ponce.**

"Welcome to Puerto Rico, Adan."

Stocky Uncle Ulise had tiny blue eyes in a round, red face and big, strong arms. Adan was excited after his first plane ride. He hugged Uncle Ulise even harder than Uncle Ulise hugged him.

---

tío (tē′ ō), uncle.
Ponce (pôn′ sā), a city in southern Puerto Rico.

"Come, we'll drive to Corral Viejo." He winked at Adan's father. "I'm sorry you didn't arrive yesterday. Yesterday was a wonderful yagua day."

"Tío Ulise, you know about yagua days too?"

"Sure. They're my favorite days."

"But wouldn't today be a good yagua day?"

"The worst. The sun's out!"

In an old jeep, they rode up into the mountains.

"Look!" said Uncle Ulise, pointing at a river jumping rocks. "Your mother and father, Jorge, and I played in that river when we were children."

They bounced up a hill to a cluster of bright houses. Many people were outside.

"This is your family, Adan," said Uncle Ulise.

Everyone crowded around the jeep. There were old and young people, and blond-, brown-, and black-haired people. There were dark-skinned and light-skinned people and blue-eyed, brown-eyed, and green-eyed people. Adan had not known there were so many people in his family. Uncle Ulise's wife, Carmen, hugged Adan and kissed both his cheeks.

The whole family sat under wide trees and ate rice, pork, vegetables, and dumplings. Adan talked and sang until his voice turned to a squeak. He ate until his stomach almost popped a pants button. Afterward he fell asleep under a big mosquito net. He was asleep even before the sun had gone down behind the mountains.

In the morning Uncle Ulise called out, "Adan, everyone ate all the food in the house. Let's get more."

"From a bodega?"

"No, **mi amor**—from my finca near the top of the mountain."

"You drive a tractor and a plow on the mountain?"

Tía Carmen smiled with her eyes. "We don't need tractors and plows on our finca."

"I don't understand."

"Come on. You will."

Adan and his parents, Aunt Carmen, and Uncle Ulise hiked up the mountain beside a splashy stream.

Near the top they walked through groves of fruit trees.

"Long ago your grandfather planted these trees," Adan's mother said. "Now Aunt Carmen and Uncle Ulise pick what they need for themselves. They give some away and sell some in Ponce."

"Let's work!" said Aunt Carmen.

Sitting on his father's shoulders, Adan picked oranges. Swinging a hooked stick, he pulled down **mangós.** Finally, gripping a very long pole, he struck down coconuts.

---

mi amor (mē ä mor′), my love.
tía (tē′ ä), aunt.
mangó (man gō′), a sweet tropical fruit, golden when ripe.

"How do we get all the food down the mountain?" he asked.

"Watch," said Aunt Carmen. She whistled loudly.

Adan saw a patch of white moving in the trees. A horse with a golden mane appeared.

Uncle Ulise fed him a mangó. The horse twitched its ears and munched the delicious fruit loudly.

"Palomo will help us carry all the fruit and vegetables we're picking," Adan's mother said.

Back at the house, Adan gave Palomo another mangó.

"Palomo will go back up to the finca now," his father said. "It's got all it wants to eat there."

Uncle Ulise rubbed his knee.

"What's the matter?" asked Adan's mother.

"My knee. It always hurts just before the rain comes."

Adan looked at the cloudless sky. "But it's not going to rain."

"Yes, it will. My knee never lies. It'll rain tonight. Maybe tomorrow. Say! When it does, it'll be a yagua day!"

In the morning Adan woke up feeling cozy under his mosquito net. He heard rain banging on the metal roof. He jumped out of bed and got a big surprise. His mother and father, Uncle Ulise, and Aunt Carmen were on the porch wearing bathing suits.

"Come, Adan," his father said. "It's a wonderful yagua day. Put on your bathing suit!"

In the forest he heard shouts and swishing noises in the rain. Racing into a clearing, he saw boys and girls shooting down a runway of grass. Then they quickly disappeared over a rock ledge.

Uncle Ulise picked up a canoe-like object from the grass. "This is yagua, Adan. It fell from this palm tree."

"And this is what we do with it," said his father. He ran, then bellyflopped on the yagua. He skimmed down the grass, sailed up into the air, and vanished over the ledge. His mother found another yagua and did the same.

"Papi! Mami!"

Uncle Ulise laughed. "Don't worry, Adan. They won't hurt themselves. The river is down there. It pools beneath the ledge. The rain turns the grass butter-slick so you can zip into the water. That's what makes it a yagua day! Come and join us!"

That day Adan found out what fun a yagua day is!

Two weeks later Adan lifted a box of mangós off the truck back in New York.

"Hola! Welcome home!"

Adan smiled at Jorge. "Why do you look sad, **compadre?**"

"Too much mail! Too much sun!"

"What you need is a yagua day."

"So you know what a yagua day is?"

"I had six yagua days in Puerto Rico."

"You went over the ledge?"

"Of course."

"Into the river?"

"Sí! Sí! Into the river. Sliding on yaguas!"

---

papi (pä′ pē), daddy.
mami (mä′ mē), mommy.
compadre (kom pä′ dre), pal.

"Two-wheeled or four-wheeled yaguas?"

Adan laughed. "Yaguas don't have wheels. They come from palm trees."

"I thought they came from panel trucks like mine."

"Nothing grows in trucks, Jorge. These mangós and oranges come from trees. Compadre, wake up. Don't you know?"

Jorge laughed. "Come, let's talk with your parents. I want to hear all about your visit to Corral Viejo!"

Glossary

a bil i ty (ə bil′ ə tē), power to do some special thing; talent. *n.*

ab sorb (ab sôrb′), take in and hold. *v.*

ac cor di on (ə kôr′ dē ən), a musical wind instrument. *n.*

ach ing (āk′ ing), suffering continuous pain. *adj.*

ac ro bat (ak′ rə bat), a person who can swing on a trapeze, walk a tightrope, do feats of bodily skill and strength. *n.*

ac tiv i ty (ak tiv′ ə tē), an action; thing to do. *n.*

ac tu al (ak′ chü əl), real; existing as a fact. *adj.*

ad lib (ad lib′), make up as one goes along. *v.*

ad vice (ad vīs′), an opinion about what should be done. *n.*

a larm (ə lärm′), sudden fear; excitement caused by fear of danger. *n.*

al ti tude (al′ tə tüd), a high place: *At some altitudes snow never melts. n.*

a maze ment (ə māz′ mənt), great surprise; sudden wonder. *n.*

an cient (ān′ shənt), belonging to times long past. *adj.*

ap plaud (ə plôd′), show approval by clapping hands or shouting. *v.*

arch (ärch), bend into a curve. *v.*

ar my (är′ mē), a large group of soldiers trained for war. *n.*

as sist ant (ə sis′ tənt), a helper; aide: *She was my assistant in the library for a time. n.*

as ton ish ing (əs ton′ ish ing), very surprising. *adj.*

at ten tion (ə ten′ shən), act of listening and watching closely: *The children paid attention to the teacher's explanations. n.*

a vail a ble (ə vā′ lə bəl), that can be used. *adj.*

av er age (av′ ər ij), usual amount. *n.*

bait (bāt), anything, especially food, used to attract fish or other animals. *n.*

bal ance (bal′ əns), put or keep in a steady position. *v.*

bale (bāl), a large bundle of material which is securely wrapped. *n.*

bal lad (bal′ əd), a poem that tells a story. *n.*

be drag gled (bi dragʹ əld), soiled by being dragged in the dirt. *adj.*

be tray (bi trāʹ), give away to the enemy; be unfaithful to. *v.*

blow fish (blōʹ fish), any of various fishes capable of inflating the body with water or air. *n.*

blunt (blunt), without a sharp edge or point. *adj.*

bold (bōld), rude: *The bold little boy made faces at us as we passed. adj.*

bor der (bôrʹ dər), the side, edge, or boundary of anything: *The scarf has a blue border. n.*

bound (bound), on the way; going: *I am bound for home. adj.*

bow (bō), a strip of wood bent by a string that is used for shooting arrows; something curved like a bow: *A rainbow is a bow. n.*

box wood (boksʹ wu̇d′), the hard, fine-grained wood of the box tree. *n.*

bram ble (bramʹ bəl), a shrub with branches covered with thorns. *n.*

breeze (brēz), a light, gentle wind. *n.*

bur ly (bėrʹ lē), big and strong; sturdy. *adj.*

bus y bod y (bizʹ ē bod′ ē), a person who meddles in the affairs of others. *n.*

ca fé (ka fāʹ), a restaurant. *n.*

ca noe (kə nüʹ), a light boat moved with a paddle held in the hands. *n.*

ca pa ble (kāʹ pə bl), able; having fitness, power, or ability. *adj.*

car a van (karʹ ə van), a group traveling together for safety. *n.*

car i bou (karʹ ə bü), any of several kinds of North American reindeer. *n.*

cart wheel (kärtʹ hwēl′), a sideways handspring or somersault. *n.*

cau tious ly (kôʹ shəs lē), very carefully. *adv.*

cease (sēs), stop. *v.*

ce ment (sə mentʹ), a fine, gray powder which, when mixed with water, becomes hard as stone. *n.*

cen ti pede (senʹ tə pēd), a flat, wormlike animal with many pairs of legs. *n.*

clam (klam), a small animal with a soft body and a shell in two hinged halves. *n.*

clam chow der (klam chouʹ dər), a thick soup or stew made with clams. *n.*

---

hat, āge, fär; let, ēqual, tėrm; it, īce; hot, ōpen, ôrder; oil, out; cup, pu̇t, rüle; ch, child; ng, long; sh, she; th, thin; ᴛʜ, then; zh, measure; ə represents *a* in about, *e* in taken, *i* in pencil, *o* in lemon, *u* in circus.

clear ing (klir′ ing), an open space of cleared land in a forest. *n.*

clog (klog), a shoe with a thick, wooden sole. *n.*

cluster (klus′ tər), a number of things of the same group growing or grouped together: *a cluster of grapes.* *n.*

coax (kōks), persuade by soft words. *v.*

col umn (kol′ əm), something slender and upright: *a column of smoke.* *n.*

com fort (kum′ fərt), ease the grief or sorrow of. *v.*

com mo tion (kə mō′ shən), violent movement; confusion; disturbance. *n.*

con science (kon′ shəns), a sense of right and wrong. *n.*

con tin u ous (kən tin′ yü əs), connected, unbroken; without a stop. *adj.*

con ven tion (kən ven′ shən), a meeting arranged for some particular purpose. *n.*

con ver sa tion (kən′ ver sā′ shən), friendly talk. *n.*

coo (kü), murmur softly. *v.*

Co-op (kō′ op), short for *Cooperative;* a store owned and operated by those who use it. *n.*

cord (kord), thick string. *n.*

cot tage (kot′ ij), a small house. *n.*

count (kount), a nobleman about equal in rank to an English earl. *n.*

cour te ous (ker′ tē əs), polite. *adj.*

co zy (kō′ zē), warm and comfortable. *adj.*

crea ture (krē′ chər), any living person or animal. *n.*

crick et (krik′ it), a black insect related to the grasshopper. Male crickets make a chirping noise by rubbing their front wings together. *n.*

criss crossed (kris′ krôst′), marked or covered with crossed lines; crosswise. *adj.*

cud (kud), a mouthful of food brought back from the stomach of cattle for second chewing. *n.*

cure (kyůr), a medicine that makes one well. *n.*

cur i os i ty (kyur′ ē os′ ə tē), eager wish to know. *n.*

dachs hund (däks′ hůnt′), a small dog with a long body and very short legs. *n.*

dam aged (dam′ ijd), harmed or injured. *adj.*

dan de li on (dan′ dl ī′ ən), a weed with bright yellow flowers. *n.*

de clare (di kler′), say, make known. *v.*

de fend (di fend′), guard from attack or harm; protect. *v.*

dem on stra tion (dem′ ən strā′ shən), clear proof. *n.*

de sire (di zīr′), a wish. *n.*

des per ate ly (des′ pər it lē), in a hopeless manner. *adv.*

dew (dü), moisture from the air that collects in small drops. *n.*

dis ap point ment (dis′ ə point′ mənt), the feeling one has after not getting what was expected or hoped for. *n.*

dis play (dis plā′), a showing of a thing to attract attention: *the dinosaur bones were on display. n.*

dis tance (dis′ təns), place far away. *n.*

do do (dō′ dō), a large, clumsy bird not able to fly. *n.*

dom i no (dom′ ə nō), any of the pieces of bone or wood marked with spots and used in playing dominoes. *n.*

dread ful ly (dred′ fəl lē), very; terribly. *adv.*

droop (drüp), hang down; bend down. *v.*

dump ling (dump′ ling), a rounded piece of dough, boiled or steamed and usually served with meat. *n.*

dwell er (dwel′ ər), a person who dwells or lives: *A city dweller lives in a city. n.*

ea ger ly (ē′ gər lē), in an enthusiastic, interested manner. *adv.*

eag let (ē′ glit), a young eagle. *n.*

ease (ēz), freedom from pain or trouble. *n.*

em bar rassed (em bar′ əst), feeling uneasy and ashamed. *adj.*

em broi dered (em broi′ dərd), decorated with a pattern of stitches. *adj.*

em per or (em′ pər ər), a man who is the ruler of an empire. *n.*

en chant ed (en chant′ id), greatly delighted. *adj.*

en e my (en′ ə mē), one who is against; not a friend. *n.*

e vent (i vent′), an important happening: *The discovery of America was a great event. n.*

ev i dent ly (ev′ ə dənt′ lē), easily seen or understood; clearly. *adv.*

ex claim (ek sklām′), cry out in surprise. *v.*

ex per i ment (ek sper′ ə ment), make a trial or test to find out something. *v.*

ex plode (ek splōd′), burst forth. *v.*

ex treme ly (ek strēm′ lē), much more than usual. *adj.*

fa mil iar (fə mil′ yər), well-known. *adj.*

fan ta sy (fan′ tə sē), imagination; play of the mind. *n.*

---

hat, āge, fär; let, ēqual, tėrm; it, īce; hot, ōpen, ôrder; oil, out; cup, pu̇t, rüle; ch, child; ng, long; sh, she; th, thin; ᴛʜ, then; zh, measure; ə represents *a* in about, *e* in taken, *i* in pencil, *o* in lemon, *u* in circus.

feel er (fē′ lər), a special part of an animal's body for touching: *A cat's whiskers are its feelers. n.*
fierce (firs), wild. *adj.*
fie ry (fi′ rē), burning, flaming. *adj.*
fig ure (fig′ yər), think, consider. *v.*
fleet (flēt), a group which moves together. *n.*
flick (flik), move with a jerk. *v.*
fling (fling), throw; throw with force. *v.*
flut ter (flut′ ər), wave back and forth quickly and lightly. *v.*
fond (fond), loving; liking; *fond of children. adj.*
force (fors), strength; power. *n.*
fo reign (for′ ən), strange; not belonging. *adj.*
for tune-tell er (fôr′ chən tel′ ər), a person who claims to be able to tell what is going to happen to people. *n.*
fret (fret), worry. *v.*
fron tier (frun tir′), of or belonging to the farthest part of a settled country, where the wilds begin. *adj.*
froth (frôth), give out foam. *v.*
fur y (fyůr′ ē), a rage; a storm of anger. *n.*

gen ius (jē′ nyəs), a person having great natural power of mind. *n.*
gla cier (glā′ shər), a large mass of ice moving slowly down a mountain or valley. *n.*
gov ern ment (guv′ ərn mənt), the ruling of a country state, or city. *n.*
grad u al (graj′ ü əl), little by little. *adj.*
grain el e va tor (grān el′ ə vā′ tər), a building for lifting or storing the seeds of plants like wheat, oats, and corn. *n.*
grate ful (grāt′ fəl), thankful for a favor received. *adj.*
graze (grāz), feed on growing grass. *v.*
grove (grōv), a group of trees standing together. *n.*
gruff (gruf), deep and harsh. *adj.*
grunt (grunt), make a deep, hoarse sound. *v.*
guin ea (gin′ ē), a fowl somewhat like a pheasant with dark-grey feathers and small, white spots. *n.*

hand i work (han′ dē wėrk′), work done by a person's hands. *n.*
har poon (här pun′), a spear with a rope tied to it. *n.*
hast i ly (hā′ stl ē), in a hurried way. *adv.*
heart y (här′ tē), warm and friendly. *adj.*
hick or y (hik′ ər ē), a North American tree whose nuts are good to eat. *n.*

ho ri zon (hə rī′ zn), a line where earth and sky seem to meet. *n.*

hushed (husht), silent; quiet. *adj.*

ice berg (īs′ bėrg′), a large mass of ice floating in the sea. *n.*

ig loo (ig′ lü), an Eskimo hut that is shaped like a dome, often built of blocks of hard snow. *n.*

ig nor ant (ig′ nər ənt), knowing little or nothing. *adj.*

im age (im′ ij), a likeness or copy: *You will see your image in this mirror. n.*

im i tate (im′ ə tāt), try to be like. *v.*

im mense (i mens′), very big; huge; vast. *adj.*

im pres sive (im pres′ iv), able to have a strong effect on the mind or feelings. *adj.*

in no cent (in′ ə sənt), doing no wrong. *adj.*

in stant ly (in′ stənt lē), at once. *adv.*

in sult (in sult′), say or do something rude or harsh. *v.*

in ter view (in′ tər vyü), a visit and talk with someone: *The reporter had an interview with the actor. n.*

i vor y (ī′ vər ē), a hard, white substance making up the tusks of elephants or walruses. *n.*

kid (kid), the leather made from the skin of a young goat. *n.*

la bor (lā′ bər), work, toil: *The carpenter was well paid for her labor. n.*

lan ky (langk′ ē), tall and thin. *adj.*

laun dry (lôn′ drē), clothes washed or to be washed. *n.*

learn ed (lėr′ nid), showing great knowledge. *adj.*

limb (lim), a leg, arm, or wing. *n.*

loft (lôft), the space just below the roof in a cabin. *n.*

lunge (lunj), move suddenly forward; thrust. *v.*

mar ma lade (mär′ mə lād), a preserve similar to jam, made of fruit. *n.*

me di um (mē′ dē əm), a person through whom messages from the spirits of the dead are supposedly sent to the living. *n.*

---

hat, āge, fär; let, ēqual, tėrm; it, īce; hot, ōpen, ôrder; oil, out; cup, pu̇t, rüle; ch, child; ng, long; sh, she; th, thin; ᴛʜ, then; zh, measure; ə represents *a* in about, *e* in taken, *i* in pencil, *o* in lemon, *u* in circus.

meek ly (mēk′ lē), mildly; patiently. *adv.*

men tion (men′ shən), speak about. *v.*

mer chant (mėr′ chənt), a person who buys and sells. *n.*

midst (midst), the middle: *in the midst of them. n.*

mim ic (mim′ ik), make fun of by imitating. *v.*

mine (mīn), dig in the earth for coal or other minerals. *v.*

min er al (min′ ər əl), a substance obtained by mining or digging in the earth: *Coal and gold are minerals. n.*

min now (min′ ō), a very small fish. *n.*

mis er a ble (miz′ ər ə bəl), very unhappy; mean. *adj.*

mis tress (mis′ tris), a woman who is the head of a house. n.

monk (mungk), a man who devotes his life to religion and lives in a house called a *monastery. n.*

mourn (môrn), grieve; feel or show sorrow over. *v.*

mu le teer (mū′ lə tir′), a person who drives mules. *n.*

mut ter (mut′ ər), speak low and unclearly. *v.*

nerv ous (ner′ vəs), restless or uneasy. *adj.*

nuz zle (nəz′ əl), touch with the nose. *v.*

o be di ent (ō bē′ dē ənt), doing what one is told to do. *adj.*

or di nar i ly (ôrd′ n er′ ə lē), usually: *Dad ordinarily makes popcorn on Saturday nights. adv.*

out er most (ou′ tər mōst), farthest out. *adj.*

oys ter (oi′ stər), a kind of shellfish or mollusk used as food. *n.*

palm (päm), any of many kinds of trees growing in warm climates. *n.*

par ka (pär′ kə), a fur jacket with a hood. *n.*

pas sage (pas′ ij), a way through. *n.*

pause (pôz), stop for a time; wait. *v.*

peace ful (pēs′ fəl), quiet; calm; full of peace. *adj.*

peas ant (pez′ nt), a farmer of the working class in Europe. *n.*

ped dler (ped′ lər), a person who travels about selling things. *n.*

peer (pir), look closely to see clearly. *v.*

per i win kle (per′ ē wing′ kəl), a low evergreen plant with blue flowers. *n.*

per suade (pər swād′), win over to do or believe. *v.*

pes ter (pes′ tər), annoy; trouble. *v.*

pet ri fied (pet′ rə fīd), very frightened. *adj.*

pi rate (pī′ rit), a person who attacks and robs ships. *n.*

plain (plān), a flat stretch of land. *n.*

plane (plān), a carpenter's tool with a blade for smoothing wood. *n.*

plat form (plat′ fôrm), a raised level surface. *n.*

pleas ure (plezh′ ər), the feeling of being pleased; delight; joy. *n.*

plight (plīt), a condition or situation, usually bad. *n.*

plod (plod), walk heavily; trudge. *v.*

plow (plou), a big, heavy farm instrument for cutting the soil and turning it over. *n.*

poppy (pop′ ē), a kind of plant with delicate, showy, red, yellow, or white flowers. *n.*

por trait (pôr′ trit), a picture of a person, especially of the face. *n.*

pos ses sion (pə zesh′ ən), a thing possessed; property: *Please move your possessions from my room. n.*

post (pōst), a piece of wood, metal, or other substance firmly set up, usually to support something. *n.*

po tion (pō′ shən), a drink, especially one used as a medicine or poison, or in magic. *n.*

prair ie (prer′ ē), a large area of level or rolling land with grass but few or no trees. *n.*

prance (prans), spring about on the hind legs: *Horses prance when they feel lively. v.*

pre cise ly (pri sīs′ lē), exactly. *adv.*

prim rose (prim′ rōz′), any of a large group of plants with flowers of various colors. *n.*

pro ceed (prə sēd′), go on after having stopped; move forward. *v.*

pro file (prō′ fīl), a side view, especially of the face. *n.*

prop (prop), hold up an object by placing it against something. *v.*

pro test (prō test′), disagree; object. *v.*

psy chol o gist (sī kol′ ə jist), an expert in *psychology*, a science which tries to explain why people act and feel as they do. *n.*

pul ley (pu̇l′ ē), a wheel with a hollowed rim in which a rope can run and so lift weights. *n.*

quar rel (kwôr′ əl), argue, fight with words. *v.*

quiv er (kwiv′ ər), shake; shiver; tremble. *v.*

---

hat, āge, fär; let, ēqual, tėrm; it, īce; hot, ōpen, ôrder; oil, out; cup, pu̇t, rüle; ch, child; ng, long; sh, she; th, thin; ᴛʜ, then; zh, measure; ə represents *a* in about, *e* in taken, *i* in pencil, *o* in lemon, *u* in circus.

rai sin (rā′ zn), a sweet, dried grape. *n.*

rare (rer), seldom seen or found. *adj.*

re cov er (ri kuv′ ər), get back (something lost, taken away, or stolen). *v.*

rel a tive (rel′ ə tiv), a person who belongs to the same family as another, such as a father, brother, aunt, nephew, or cousin. *n.*

re lief (ri lēf′), the lessening of, or freeing from, a pain, burden, or difficulty. *n.*

re mark a ble (ri mar′ kə bəl), worthy of notice; unusual. *adj.*

re ply (ri plī′), answer by words or action: *He replied with a shout. v.*

re sem ble (ri zem′ bl), to be like in form, figure, or qualities. *v.*

re stock (rē stok′), lay in a supply of again. *v.*

ring let (ring′ lit), a curl: *She wears her hair in ringlets. n.*

ru in (rü′ ən), destroy; spoil. *v.*

sat is fied (sat′ i sfīd), feeling contented. *adj.*

sau cer (sô′ sər), a small dish to set a cup on. *n.*

sav age (sav′ ij), fierce, cruel, ready to fight. *adj.*

scam per (skam′ pər), run quickly. *v.*

scarce (skers), hard to get; rare. *adj.*

sci en tif ic (sī′ ən tif′ ik), using the facts and laws of science. *adj.*

scorch ing (skôrch ing), very hot; burning. *adj.*

scur ry (skėr′ ē), run quickly; scamper; hurry. *v.*

seize (sēz), take hold of suddenly; grasp. *v.*

sense (sens), be aware of; feel. *v.*

ser i ous (sir′ ē əs), thoughtful; grave. *adj.*

set back (set′ bak′), a check to progress; defeat. *n.*

set tler (set′ lər), a person who settles in a new country. *n.*

sky lark (skī′ lärk′), a small bird that sings very sweetly. *n.*

slim (slim), thin. *adj.*

slope (slōp), land that goes up or down at an angle. *n.*

slum ber (slum′ bər), a light sleep. *n.*

snarl (snärl), growl sharply and show one's teeth. *v.*

snatch (snach), seize suddenly. *v.*

sog gy (sog′ ē), soaked; thoroughly wet. *adj.*

sor row ful (sor′ ə fəl), full of sorrow; sad. *adj.*

spade (spād), a tool for digging; kind of shovel. *n.*

spir its (spir′ its), a state of mind; temper. *n.*

splen did (splen′ did), brilliant; glorious; magnificent; grand. *adj.*

spring (spring), leap or jump. *v.* **sprang,** *past tense.*

squab ble (skwob′ əl), take part in a noisy quarrel about something unimportant. *v.*

string (string), put on a thread. *v.*

su per sti tion (sü′ pər stish′ ən), an unreasoning fear of what is unknown or mysterious. *n.*

sup plies (sə plīz′), the food and equipment necessary for an army, expedition, or the like. *n.*

sup port (sə pôrt′), keep from falling; hold up. *v.*

swap (swop), trade. *v.*

swear (swer), promise; vow. *v.* **swore,** *past tense.*

swish (swish), move with a thin, light, or brushing sound. *v.*

tan gled (tang′ gəld), twisted together in a confused mass. *adj.*

tat tered (tat′ ərd), torn; ragged. *adj.*

tel e scope (tel′ ə skōp), an instrument for making distant objects appear nearer and larger: *Telescopes are used to study the stars. n.*

tem per a ture (tem′ pər ə chər), a degree of heat or cold. *n.*

ter ri fied (ter′ ə fīd), filled with great fear. *adj.*

ter ri to ry (ter′ ə tôr′ ē), a land; region. *n.*

ter ror (ter′ ər), a great fear. *n.*

thick et (thik′ it), shrubs, bushes, or small trees growing close together. *n.*

this tle (this′ əl), a plant with prickly leaves. *n.*

tim id ly (tim′ id lē), shyly. *adv.*

tof fy (tô′ fē), one type of candy; taffy. *n.*

trans par ent (tran sper′ ənt), easily seen through. *adj.*

tra peze (trə pēz′), a short, horizontal bar hung by ropes like a swing. *n.*

trem bling (trem′ bling), shaking because of fear, cold, or the like. *adj.*

tri bal (trī′ bəl), relating to a group of people who are joined by race and customs under the same leader. *adj.*

tri fle (trī′ fəl), a thing that is of very little value or importance. *n.*

trot (trot), go at a pace between a walk and a run. *v.*

un set tled (un set′ ld), not calm. *adj.*

---

hat, āge, fär; let, ēqual, tėrm; it, īce; hot, ōpen, ôrder; oil, out; cup, pu̇t, rüle; ch, child; ng, long; sh, she; th, thin; ᴛʜ, then; zh, measure; ə represents *a* in about, *e* in taken, *i* in pencil, *o* in lemon, *u* in circus.

up right (up′ rīt′), standing up straight; erect. *adj.*

up roar (up′ rôr′), a noisy disturbance. *n.*

var y (ver′ ē), change; make or become different. *v.*

vast (vast), very, very large; immense. *adj.*

vein (vān), one of the blood vessels that carry blood to the heart from all parts of the body. *n.*

waist coat (wāst′ kōt′ or wes′ kət), a man's vest.

wal rus (wôl′ rəs), a large sea animal of the arctic regions, resembling a seal but having long tusks. *n.*

wand (wond), a thin stick or rod. *n.*

wares (werz), articles for sale. *n.*

wear y (wir′ ē), tired. *adj.*

were wolf (wir′ wulf′), in folklore, a person who can change into a wolf. *n.*

whirl wind (hwėrl′ wind), whirling storm of wind. *n.*

whit tle (hwit′ l), cut shavings or chips (from wood) with a knife. *v.*

wil der ness (wil′ dər nis), a wild place; region with no people living in it. *n.*

wisp (wisp), a small portion; slight bit. *n.*

worth (wėrth), equal in value to: *This book is worth five dollars. adj.*

wreck (rek), the destruction of a ship, building, train, car, or airplane: *The storm caused many wrecks. n.*

wretch ed (rech′ id), very unfortunate or unhappy. *adj.*

wrig gle (rig′ əl), move by twisting and turning. *v.*

zig zag (zig′ zag′), move with short, sharp turns from one side to the other. *v.*

---

hat, āge, fär; let, ēqual, tėrm; it, īce; hot, ōpen, ôrder; oil, out; cup, pu̇t, rüle; ch, child; ng, long; sh, she; th, thin; ᴛʜ, then; zh, measure; ə represents *a* in about, *e* in taken, *i* in pencil, *o* in lemon, *u* in circus.

"The Broken Toothpick" adapted from *Abracadabra!* Copyright © 1975 by Barbara Seuling. Reprinted by permission of Julian Messner, a Simon & Schuster division of Gulf & Western Corporation.

"Frederick," specified adaptation from *Frederick* by Leo Lionni. Copyright © 1967 by Leo Lionni. Reprinted by permission of Pantheon Books, a Division of Random House, Inc.

"Pitseolak: Pictures out of My Life" from *Pitseolak: Pictures out of my life* from recorded interviews by Dorothy Eber. Copyright © 1971. University of Washington Press. By permission of Rolf Harder & Associates and the author.

"How Bambi Found the Meadow" excerpted from *Bambi* by Felix Salten. Copyright © 1928, 1956 by Simon & Schuster, Inc. Reprinted by permission of Simon & Schuster, a Division of Gulf & Western Corporation.

Art Credits

Howard Berelson: pp. 188–195, 197–206, 208–213; David Brown: p. 90; Diane deGroat: pp. 146–151; Pam Ford: p. 214; Hal Frenck: pp. 77, 79–84, 86, 87, 258, 259, 261–265, 267, 269, 271; Ethel Gold: pp. 231–234, 237, 238, 240–244, 246–248; Les Gray: pp. 27, 29–38, 40–43; Marion Krupp: pp. 2–4, 6, 8–10, 12, 14, 92–96; Karen Milone: pp. 114, 116–125; Diane Paterson: p. 152; Pitseolak: pp. 66, 69, 71, 73; Jan Pyk: pp. 44, 45, 126, 128, 130, 131, 133, 135–137, 139–144; Anthony Rao: pp. 16–19, 21–23, 25, 26, 97, 99, 100, 102–105, 107, 109, 111, 230; Steven Schindler: pp. 154–156, 158, 159, 161–165, 167–171, 173, 174; Clifford Schule: pp. 48, 51, 54, 55, 57, 59, 61, 63, 65; Sue Thompson: pp. 112, 113; Lynn Uhde: pp. 74–76; James Watling: pp. 249, 251–257; Jennie Williams: pp. 184–187.

Photo Credits

Cover photo: Gene Anthony/Black Star; p. 1: Dana Hyde/Photo Researchers; p. 46: Jonathon T. Wright/Bruce Coleman; p. 47: John V.A.F. Neal/Photo Researchers; p. 88: Diane Rawson/Photo Researchers; p. 89: Russ Kinne/Photo Researchers; p. 91: Bill Binzen/The Image Bank; p. 153: John Lewis Stage/The Image Bank; pp. 176–183: Michal Heron; p. 215: Harald Sund/The Image Bank; pp. 216–220, 222, 224, 226, 227, 229: Michal Heron.

3 5 7 9 11 13 15 17 19 20 18 16 14 12 10 8 6 4 2